Living with CMT

A Mother and Son Journey through Charcot Marie Tooth Disease

By Dawn Johnson

A true-life account of navigating a rare disease

Disclaimer: This memoir is strictly my own recollections as someone who has the inherited condition known as Charcot-Marie-Tooth Disease. It includes news, information and firsthand accounts about the disease but is not intended to be a substitute for professional medical advice, diagnosis, or treatment. Always seek the advice of your physician or other qualified health providers with any questions you may have regarding a medical condition. Never disregard professional medical advice or delay in seeking it because of something you have read in this memoir.

Published by SuburbanBuzz.com LLC

ISBN: 978-1-7360820-0-3

DEDICATION

In memory of my son and only child, Ryan William Schaeffer
July 19, 1998 – December 25, 2018
Don't think of him as gone away
his journey's just begun,
life holds so many facets
this earth is only one.
Just think of him as resting
from the sorrows and the tears
in a place of warmth and comfort
where there are no days and years.
Think how he must be wishing
that we could know today
how nothing but our sadness
can really pass away.
And think of him as living
in the hearts of those he touched…
for nothing loved is ever lost
and he was loved so much.
~ Ellen Brenneman

CONTENTS

ACKNOWLEDGMENTS

I would like to thank everyone who supported me through the process of writing this book. I would like to especially like to thank Becky Raines, Scott LeBleu, Dr. Luquette, Janece Sulephen, Ruth Lerro and Frank Creswell for their steadfast support during the project.

I first began writing while dating Frank Creswell, who proposed somewhere around the middle chapters. I said, "Yes!" After tying the knot, we honeymooned at Disney World—a wonderful vacation destination for people with disabilities. We're still in the honeymoon phase, and I can't say it enough: I love you to the moon and back, Frank. Thank you for always being my pillar of strength through all the joy and pain.

The reflections of Amy Anderson Gerlach, my best friend since middle school, appear in some of the chapters. Her contributions are much appreciated and provide a unique perspective in the book.

I also want to acknowledge Sherrie Anderson, CP, LPO, of Anderson Orthopedics and Prosthetics. She has been so instrumental in my journey and does such good work for her clients and people in the mission field. She made Ryan's first ankle supports and donated Ryan's braces after his death as his posthumous gift to Africa.

Linda Perkins was a wonderful source of comfort after my son's funeral and provided much of the food after the service, as well as a few days after.

I also thank my editor Melanie Saxton for working with me throughout the writing of this book and becoming a friend and advocate in the process.

INTRODUCTION

Disability is a matter of perception. If you can do just one thing well, you're needed by someone.
~ Martina Navratilova

My son Ryan passed away on Christmas Day, 2018, at the age of twenty. He had come home to Douglass, Texas, for the holidays after moving out on his own. None of us suspected that this would be his final visit. Never in my worst nightmare did I think I'd lose my only child.

Ryan, like me, suffered from Charcot Marie Tooth Disease, an inherited and rare neuromuscular condition otherwise known as CMT. The disease is not fatal and did not cause Ryan's death. The autopsy revealed that he died from lymphocytic myocarditis, which basically means his lungs filled with fluid, and his heart couldn't take it. No one had a clue he had the condition.

Ryan and I began collaborating on this book six months prior to his passing, totally unaware that he wouldn't be here to see it in print. Perhaps you can imagine the utter shock and devastation at his unexpected passing. In my sorrow and panic, it felt like I was swimming through molasses, almost paralyzed at this terrible loss. I must say, though, that I was compelled to keep motoring on, knowing that the project meant a lot to Ryan. I was determined to see it through for his sake, and in the process, realized that many lives would be touched through the words, sentiments, experiences and resources in the book.

My goal has always been to share what living with a disability is like and spread awareness about CMT. Ryan wanted to contribute his perspective as a child who was diagnosed and grew to adulthood while navigating the disease. In my grief, I have continued to write in his honor about the disease, but also the many wonderful remembrances of his friends and our family. I think Ryan's short journey proves, without a doubt, that people with disabilities can touch lives, uplift others, and add sprinkles of wonderment and light into the world. He was so loved.

It's been incredibly difficult adjusting to this new reality of life without Ryan. The wound is raw, but his influence on many lives, mine included, keeps me going. My husband Frank, whom I married during the writing of this book, has been my rock. You'll see his name throughout the pages as a living example of "in sickness and in health" and as someone who has partnered in the journey with me.

Frank is a tremendous blessing, along with my dear friend since middle school, Amy Anderson Gerlach. Her voice, too, appears in the book as someone with a firsthand perspective of my life as a CMT survivor.

***

Charcot Marie Tooth Disease. It sounds like something a dental hygienist would say. Or an orthodontist. It certainly does have a misleading moniker. Actually, CMT has nothing to do with teeth and everything to do with neurological, muscular dystrophy-like symptoms. It's called CMT for short.

What exactly is CMT? That was something I was destined to learn, whether I liked it or not. No one in my family had ever heard of this mysterious thing called CMT. We were clueless when my symptoms appeared in childhood and mystified as the disease affected me. Some doctors were left scratching their heads as well.

CMT is often misdiagnosed. It's considered a "rare" progressive genetic disease, and not enough is known about it. Still, it affects about 1 in 2,500 people in the United States—around about 125,000 to 150,000 of us, although that number might be low due to undiagnosed or improperly diagnosed cases. It is one of the most common inherited neurological disorders and named for the three physicians who first identified it in 1886-Jean-Martin Charcot, Pierre Marie, and Howard Henry Tooth. The "tooth" part of the name can and does confuse the general public, which is why I prefer the acronym CMT.

You may wonder what it's like living with a neurological disease. Well, it affects people in a variety of ways. The Muscular Dystrophy Association states: "The many different types of Charcot-Marie-Tooth (CMT) are distinguished by age of onset, inheritance pattern, severity, and whether they're linked to defects in axon or myelin."

In general, CMT causes muscle weakness and nervous system dysfunctions, but there are variations. Each person is different. According to CMTUSA.org:

Since CMT is a multi-gene disorder, there are many different genes that cause the disorder when mutated. Since 1991, more than 100 different genes causing CMT have been identified and the list continues to grow. CMT can be divided into types and subtypes. The types are the clinical pictures of CMT (CMT type 1, 2, 4, X, etc.), usually defined by inheritance pattern and nerve conductions. Subtypes (CMT1A, 2B, 4C, X1, etc.) are given only when the genetic cause is known. Each subtype corresponds to a gene.

It turns out that both Ryan and I were diagnosed with CMT1A. This is the most common form of CMT, comprising about two-thirds of all cases and around sixty-six percent of all patients with CMT1. This means I have a duplication of the PMP22 gene on Chromosome 17. Instead of having two copies of the gene (one from each of my parents), there are three copies, two on one chromosome and one on the other. This particular gene causes the production of too much PMP22 protein, and my body cannot process it fast enough.

This also means I live with a chronic, severe, and debilitating inherited condition.

Yes, CMT is inherited. Some unknown person in my family tree passed the gene to me, and I passed it to my son. After searching, all my family has found is someone on my dad's side with multiple sclerosis. My dad's oldest sister had really bad tremors but no foot weakness. I think my dad has tremors in his hands, but he won't admit it. Both of my parents had their blood sent off for some kind of testing, but none of it showed CMT or anything similar. They walk just fine, thank goodness.

I, on the other hand, don't walk "just fine," at least not anymore, and no one really knows where and how I got this disease. It is degenerative in most cases, but I am thankful that CMT is not life-threatening. Both Ryan and I shared the symptoms of muscle weakness, muscle atrophy, and changes in sensation in the feet, lower legs, and hands. As far as our forearms, they never lost sensation. I have lost muscle tone but assumed that it was from me losing weight until the doctors explained it was muscle wasting away.

Research to understand this disease is ongoing. There needs to be a much deeper understanding of CMT and a better explanation for individuals who are suffering from it. I have lived since childhood with this condition—Ryan, too—and therefore feel compelled to share anything that may help people understand what this disease could entail.

Medical management is crucial, but even that can be confusing based on who dispenses advice and medication. Some CMT patients experience weakness of the respiratory muscles and have breathing difficulties. Some have sensory loss and hand, leg, ankle and foot difficulties, as well as other mobility issues. There is concern about prescription drug interactions as well.

It really is a full-time job to oversee the many "moving parts" to our daily care, but being informed and determined helps. We must be our own best advocates. Parents of children with CMT must be their advocates as well. A great portion of this book covers these issues, and I hope and pray it is a blessing to everyone reading it.

***

People also need to realize that most of us with CMT can work through our physical limitations so that the disease doesn't overtake our lives. Ryan strived hard to overcome his own limitations and make the most of his gifts and abilities. He looked to me as an example of what could be accomplished with the right attitude and philosophy. In short, the glass was always half full, not half empty. Or better yet, the glass was refillable.

We wanted to help individuals understand why a person walking down the street might have a limp or why someone may look just fine sitting in a car but need a handicap parking space. Our goal in writing this book is to help spread knowledge that leads to compassion everywhere, including schools and on playgrounds and throughout our communities. The aspects of bullying are so, so painful, whether they occur in person or on today's social media platforms.

It's frustrating, really, that I even have to mention bullying. If you or a loved one have a disability, you probably know exactly what I mean. I, personally, was on the receiving end of a lot of terrible behavior from my peers back in the day... back when society was less knowledgeable about the value of all human beings, regardless of their handicaps. Ryan was on the receiving end of some of it, much milder than I lived through, but at least my experiences prepared me to advocate for him. I knew precisely what he faced and spoke out for him—loudly when necessary, and behind the scenes, as good parents do.

At this stage in history, you would think people would already be enlightened. You would think there was room for everyone in the world, with or without disabilities. After all, everyone has worth and a mission and a calling, and our society must be reminded of that fact.

This is why it's important for all of us to advocate for those with physical or mental impairments. We who have disabilities traverse a complicated world made more complex due to our condition. I would like our fellow human beings to understand that people with CMT are not mentally or emotionally disabled…we are just like anyone else. We have the same intelligence. We have the same hopes and dreams. Just because we operate our limbs differently doesn't mean we aren't capable of holding jobs and solving problems and serving others.

Ryan was such a profound example of this. He was worthy of the same respect that anyone else enjoys and did, indeed, hold a job, pursue his education, and serve others. By the time he turned twenty, he had created his own company called Schaeffer IT (that can still be found on Facebook and Instagram as I write this book).

He was in the process of finishing his website—IT was his passion. Mind you; he ran this side business while holding down a full time IT job at the corporate headquarters of ABC Auto. I can't even begin to list the number of people who looked to him as an inspiration.

To all who are out there trying to make something of yourselves, think of Ryan as an example. He was certainly a positive influence in the world and is sorely missed. The outpouring of memories, funny stories, and heartwarming anecdotes I've received since Ryan's passing certainly help me get through each day. But more importantly, it shows me that Ryan's calling, as a twenty-year-old kid, was to bless others with his humor and impress us all with his willingness to launch himself into the world, despite his disability.

If I can spread our message of advocacy and acceptance, then the lives of many individuals suffering from CMT may be spared that dreaded look and wordless curiosity: What is wrong with you? or You look just fine, so why are you parking there? or Why are you so weird? or Why are you walking that way? People need to understand that it is not weird or strange on our part … it's simply our reality. We navigate our communities and the workplace and our family lives with the same desire to succeed and excel. The world would be a better place if people were more open to understanding differences in others. This book is a wonderful platform to do just that.

Disabled people are challenged through many different aspects of our lives. Some symptoms can be seen, and some may not be visible. But whatever our condition, it makes us unique and strong. We should not be bullied or criticized for our disabilities. We should be praised for our determination to press forward. Most of all, we should be encouraged and valued as contributing members of society.

CHAPTER 1
CHILDHOOD

Promise me you'll always remember:
You are braver than you believe, and stronger than you seem, and smarter than you think.
~ A. A. Milne from Winnie the Pooh

I love the quote above by A. A. Milne. My husband Frank had the words and some of the Pooh characters framed as artwork. I find it inspirational, especially as a person with a disability.

Never, ever did I imagine as a little girl how important that inspiration would be or that someday I'd be writing a medical memoir, for my early childhood was so carefree. My story begins in Prince George's County, Maryland, where I was born. I spent the first three years of my life in a tiny, older unit in the Glendale Apartments in Lanham, Maryland, not too far from Andrews Air Force Base and Washington D.C.

To me, these early years seemed normal. My mother says I had a typical infancy and toddlerhood, talking at around eight months and scooting around in lieu of walking. I think I was finally taking my first steps around thirteen months or so. Still, I've watched home movies of me learning to walk, and nothing about those first steps hinted at what was to come. No, my family and I were oblivious.

I enjoyed my earliest school years in Lanham, about twenty minutes north. We moved from our apartment into a house along with our white miniature poodle, Fifi. It was exciting, as this was my parents' first home purchase. I'll never forget walking into my new home and the wonderful feeling of knowing it was our very own.

I remember the huge long driveway. Dad had to wear golf shoes when he mowed the grass; the hill was so steep.

My half-sister lived with us, and Dad lost his temper with her at times. I adored him, but at the same time was terrified of him and seemed to find myself right in the middle of them. Sadly, I later became the target, a family situation that has haunted us all these years that we are still addressing. I speak in great detail about the dynamics later in the book.

We moved again, this time to a house where I made more friends. We romped around the playground at school, walked home together, and played together on weekends. We enjoyed playing outside a lot, mostly in my yard, and I recall the different games. Oh, how I loved to ride my bike. However, I was confined to the driveway and later was allowed to ride certain lengths of the sidewalk. Oh boy, if I was caught going further, I was punished. This meant spankings, usually in front of everyone. So, I was a kid who carefully minded my parents and tried hard to do the right thing … or else!

My parents did once enroll me in a Christian school, but I absolutely hated it. One downside was the very long bus ride to and from school. The uniforms and the "no talking" rule during lunch didn't help, not to mention spending very little time outside. It made for incredibly long and boring days. I remember changing out of my skirt into shorts for some sort of P.E. program, but other than that, it was a rigid environment. Thankfully, my parents put me back in public elementary school.

I have always loved to travel, and this probably has something to do with the trips I took as a child. My parents took me twice to Hawaii and to California several times. One summer, they rented a van and drove me, my sister and some cousins we picked up along the way. We enjoyed our trip across the United States. They also took me to Bermuda and Florida. Again, it was a typical childhood for that period in history, and I did the typical kid stuff.

Honestly, I never dreamed that anything "bad" would ever happen to me. I felt protected. There were no obstacles then—no inkling that my world was about to change. I'm happy, in hindsight, that I had those years of uninhibited fun. They were wonderful and included summers spent with my Aunt Janece in Orange Grove, Texas. Some of the best times occurred during those trips. It was cool being in a totally different state with such a different climate and culture. Orange Grove, located near the Gulf of Mexico, was much smaller than I was used to.

I remember how my aunt was always there to greet me at the airport as I came off the plane with the flight attendant —they were called stewardesses back then—each time I visited. In those days, there was little cause for alarm when children traveled alone. The stewardesses took good care of their young passengers. I enjoyed the attention and felt quite special on those flights.

My aunt was always so happy to see me coming up the walkway. She was the highlight of my summers and greatly enjoyed seeing how I grew year by year. She considered me her cute little blonde, blue-eyed niece, and we had a special bond. I was only with her for a month or two, once a year, and therefore she was always the first to notice anything "new" about me.

You might wonder when the symptoms of CMT struck. Well, when I was around nine or ten, my aunt seemed concerned about how I was getting around. She noticed I had difficulty walking and how the arch in my foot had gotten so high. My toes were also really curly, and she didn't understand why. I do remember her talking about it a lot during those summers.

"Look at those curly toes," my aunt would say after I woke up in the mornings. I remember sitting on her lap at the kitchen table. It was our morning ritual—our quiet time with no television or disruptions—and quite precious. She'd pick up my foot and comment and laugh, but never in a mean way. Still, I began to wonder what was wrong with my curly toes. They were different than other people's toes, but they still worked … well, kind of. I have never been able to separate my toes but didn't realize that it was a big deal.

All of my other friends could walk in her high heels when we played dress up, so why was I having so many problems doing it? Why was I slower in almost everything, like walking to a friend's house or climbing a hill?

My feet didn't hurt unless I went outside without shoes. I couldn't go barefoot on the rocks like all my friends, and walking on the concrete around the pool was also uncomfortable. There were a lot of sticker burrs in the yard, and I could not balance to pluck them out of my feet, so I normally wore shoes. These were not special shoes, by any means. I tried wearing hightop sneakers to support my ankles, but I also remember wearing sandals, which made walking more difficult because my toe sometimes dragged. I had to be careful to watch my step. It was a real accomplishment to be able to wear a pair of wedges to church. I was only able to wear them a few times because I had difficulty balancing in them.

I loved the Texas heat, but not the humidity, which was nothing like the weather up north. By the way, I loved the people in Orange Grove too. The Lone Star State grew on me so much that I eventually moved to that state much later in life. In the meantime, I felt so free in the vast countryside, swimming with friends, enjoying a variety of animals, bike riding, and playing tennis.

My aunt also took me to Corpus Christi quite often to shop. I absolutely loved those days. It was so much fun to browse the stores with her—she had such great taste and knew many people in the stores. At that age, I thought it was so cool that she got such special treatment when they recognized her. I can still remember some of the smells of those stores, especially the perfumes they sold. We shopped all day, dined out, and visited my uncle's dealerships sometimes. If I had a friend over the night before, she let them come too. It made it that much more fun. We were all so tired on the way home, and I remember sitting in the backseat and reflecting on the good times we had.

I also distinctly remember going to a little old lady's bakery. She lived locally in Orange Grove and had some of the best baked goods. On those days, we normally went to the local grocery store to stock up on goodies. Ahh, the good ole days. Back then, my disease didn't stop me from doing much or going shopping all day. Now, shopping all day isn't always possible; I tire out too quickly.

My uncle took me fishing in the nearby ponds, which was fun. Those ponds were surrounded by caliche, a white rock common in that area. It was somewhat difficult to maneuver around those rocks, but I made it happen with determination so I could enjoy time with my uncle and with my friends who played there. My aunt and uncle had all sorts of pets and livestock too, and I helped my aunt take care of the horses. There were cows, but I wasn't allowed near them. I fed the outside dogs when my uncle was late getting in. Funny, but my aunt kept a tiny white poodle indoors, which looked a lot like my mom's poodle.

My aunt and uncle also co-owned Indian Creek Ranch in Kerrville, Texas. On trips to that ranch with cousins and friends, we saw all kinds of wildlife—deer, rams, boars, and eagles. I remember my aunt being chased by a large ram across the rocks. Not surprisingly, its head is still mounted in her house to this day, ensuring it wouldn't chase anyone else. Oh—and one summer, we got to bottle feed a fawn that must have been separated from its mother. That was a special mission, keeping the poor thing alive.

I don't recall having a difficult time doing any of this or keeping up with my cousins who were with us. In fact, you name it—I was probably doing it. Those had to be some of the best vacations of my life.

Speaking of cousins, Aunt Janece's son Mark lived with my family and worked at my dad's software company. We all took a trip to Bermuda when I was around the age of twelve. We boated and rode mopeds, and it was kind of scary being on the opposite side of the road (they drove on the left instead of the right side), especially since there were lots of circles and roundabouts. I also remember going to Corpus Christi with cousin Mark much later when I was in high school. We shared a special bond. He was an IT specialist and so much more that he learned while working at my dad's software company, and I wanted to mention him posthumously (he died of brain cancer) because he influenced my son Ryan, who went to school to get the same kind of IT accreditations. Ryan learned so much about fixing the bugs in the computer, creating websites, programming and so much more. I know Mark would have been so proud of his accomplishments. I know I was a proud mom. It was something he excelled at and loved to do—he had the same drive as Mark. They talked often about computers and what he was learning in school when Mark came to visit us in Texas.

***

Fast forward to the Thanksgiving holiday of 2018 when my aunt, mother and I reminisced about those early years. During our conversation, my aunt recalled the fateful summer when I came off the airplane around the age of nine or ten, and she knew something was definitely wrong. She could not believe her eyes and thought I had been crippled, but didn't mention it to me at the time.

Now, as an adult, I listened as she shared her reaction. It just made me want to cry. I can't imagine what I looked like. This wasn't just about curly toes; she suspected it was something neurological. Honestly, at that point, I still thought I moved around normally and didn't feel self-conscious, for I didn't know any better. As a kid, I just thought I was clumsy. No big deal, right?

My aunt said she called my mom to question her about it. Mom told her she hadn't noticed anything, except that I was tripping more. My aunt agreed that tripping was a problem and thought I should see a doctor to have it checked out. She then contacted her friend, a neurologist, to see if she'd come out and observe my walking and examine my feet.

My aunt and I went swimming with the neurologist one day, although I had no idea that our visitor was a doctor of any kind. I just thought it was nice to have another person to swim with. After observing me in and out of the pool, she asked me to sit on the pool's edge. She wanted to see if I was able to lift my toes at all, and I couldn't. She then told my aunt it was definitely something neurological and should be looked at by a specialist.

Apparently, my aunt talked to my dad about all of this, but he refused to think anything was wrong with me.

"Everything is fine," he insisted—in denial, I am guessing, and not wanting to believe there was anything wrong with his child. "Send her back home."

My aunt refused, for it was still early in the summer. Instead, she dropped the subject with my dad but talked to my mom about it every chance she had. Apparently, a lot of changes were going on with my feet and ability to walk, but neither one of my parents saw it. I guess since they lived with me day to day, they just didn't notice.

Mom finally agreed to make an appointment for me before school started. That meant I had to leave Texas a bit earlier than usual, but my aunt was truly concerned and wanted me to be seen by a professional.

***

I flew home that summer, expecting to go back to school in my same town with my same friends. But instead, I arrived home to some other news. My parents announced that we were moving to New Jersey. New Jersey?! That would be another adjustment on top of being afraid of what the doctors might find. I was not excited about the move at all. I didn't want things to change, but I don't remember complaining, at least not out loud. That would have gotten me in trouble. I was one of those children who were better off being seen but not heard unless spoken too.

My mom told me that she first took me to my primary doctor and was told to see a podiatrist. The podiatrist thought I was bowlegged and suggested I try braces to correct it. This was when my mom decided to go to a neurologist, and that began my hospital journey—not to mention a whole new life in a new town and state.

We lived in the small suburban town of Bridgewater in central New Jersey, about twice the size of Lanham. I was entering Hillside Middle School and didn't know what to expect, especially coming from Maryland and starting over. Middle school, compared to elementary school, is a whole different animal. If you are lucky, you enter with classmates you already know. But there I was, entering middle school without any familiar faces at all.

Yep, I was a total stranger about to venture into a sea of adolescent angst and hormones and cliques without my friends. As you can imagine, I was nervous like any girl would be, and a bit anxious in totally unfamiliar surroundings. The "unknowns" were daunting. I was hoping to make new friends and find cool things to do.

Much to my surprise, I was worried over nothing! I did make some great new friends—two, in particular, became best friends—and our slumber parties were always fun. Mom brought home food from Roy Rogers (our favorite other than pizza), and we'd go in the basement or my room and talk until my parents went upstairs. Then we watched TV most of the night, and also listened to pop and rock music, depending on our moods. We didn't experiment much with makeup, but we did like to do our hair in all sorts of different styles. I liked staying over at my friends' houses because their parents never seemed as strict.

Overall, these friendships were more than I expected, and I was grateful for them. I couldn't ask for much more, especially being the new kid on the block. I was so fortunate to make a lifelong best friend, Amy Anderson

Gerlach, who shares her own perspective about our middle school days below:

I met Dawn when we were twelve years old. It was a transitional time for both of us. Dawn had recently moved to Bridgewater, and I was living in a neighboring town, Bound Brook. We were going through adolescence with all the physical and emotional changes that come with that. On top of it all, the two middle schools in our district consolidated when we were both in the 7th grade. The kids that had attended Adamsville Middle School were now part of Hillside Middle School. I was part of the "Adamsville Invasion," as we were lovingly referred to.

Dawn and I had our first meaningful interactions during the legendary 7th-grade class trip to Stokes State Forest in Sussex County. As fate would have it, Dawn and I ended up in a cabin together and became fast friends. At that age, Dawn's illness was very new to her, and while it was causing her some balance issues, mostly affecting her legs, she didn't have any trouble keeping up with the rest of us.

***

So, my life with CMT really started with this move to New Jersey and my introduction to a neurologist. I thought, *Why is this necessary? I don't feel that bad. I'm slow, but not that slow. What is this all about?*

My mom, too, just assumed I was an awkward and clumsy kid. For instance, I'd walk across a parking lot with her or shop with her in the stores and would trip over my own feet and fall. How embarrassing! Sometimes I'd scrape my knees and elbows, and that wasn't fun. No, I didn't like tripping all the time. It got in the way of what I wanted to do. I always brushed it off as being careless, but it was getting tiresome.

After all, I was able to run, but not that fast. Anything the other kids were doing was always harder for me, but I still managed to keep up. Balancing was a challenge. I fell frequently and tripped a lot. Even with this happening, I was just a young girl ready to face the world and have fun doing it. So despite my slips and spills, I didn't think it was necessary to see a neurologist. I felt it was a waste of my time—and perhaps I was in a bit of denial myself. Little did I know that everything was about to change. We were all in for a huge surprise, and not the good kind of surprise.

I had no idea how much I would need my friends in the near future. Friends sometimes can be the best way to cope with some of the hardest curveballs that life throws our way. After all, "disability" isn't something that comes to mind when you are a junior high student. None of us could have known what I was going to face. My family and I were in for the shock of a lifetime—something, I am quite sure, that every parent would dread for their child.

My doctor did some routine tests and announced, "I would like to do further testing to find out what the problem is that's causing you to have some weakness."

He felt fairly certain that it was a muscle disorder. In fact, he needed to do many more tests to pinpoint the actual problem.

Me and my aunt swimming together is a sweet memory.

The caliche pond where my uncle took me fishing and I rode my bike to often.

You can notice the start of my high arches and curly toes here – typical signs of CMT.

Petting the deer at Indian Creek Ranch

CHAPTER 2
DIAGNOSIS

We are stronger in the places we have been broken.
~ Ernest Hemingway

I was taken out of school in 7th grade and admitted to the Somerset County Hospital in New Jersey, which had a children's ward. This was my residence for one week, and it did not hold a favorite place in my childhood memories—far from it. What an ordeal for a little kid!

Staying in the confines of my room, alone and isolated, wasn't fun at all. It seemed like any other hospital room—no cheery child-themed paint or wallpaper. I had a TV without many channels or great reception. I was allowed to get up and move around in my room, but when I opened my door to go out in the hall, the nurses usually caught me. I was there for diagnostic testing, and the staff didn't want me to catch anything. I had access to a phone but don't recall ever using it—although my Aunt Janece reminded me recently that I did manage to call her collect from the payphone in the hallway to keep her updated. I don't have a clear memory of this, but apparently, I snuck out to make those calls, and she told me that if I heard a nurse or doctor coming, I should hang up and call her back when I could. I'm just glad she was looking out for me, even from afar. I feel she still does to this day.

I had my own bathroom and shower. Most of the time, I had to wear a hospital gown, but I did have pajama pants of my own. I mostly occupied my time with a bag I had packed filled with things I enjoyed, like my Walkman and cassettes. I was also very into all the teen magazines with the newest heartthrobs. I also had schoolwork to do, as my teachers didn't want me to fall behind.

Somewhere in between all the CT scans and blood work came a nasty test of drinking a very sweet thick liquid so they could analyze God only knows! It made me want to throw it right back up. Still, after all of that, the doctors seemed unsure.

The tests sure weren't fun—blood work analysis, MRI's and CAT scans Monday through Thursday, leading up to a final test scheduled on Friday—an excruciating muscle biopsy—just so they could figure out what was wrong with me. I do remember that my dad asked them to not give me the dye during the scans. I didn't understand why at the time, but later after having it as an adult, I now know why. It gives you some very disturbing feelings, like you are urinating, but you're not. Your mouth gets hot, as well as other side effects they tell you about in case it happens.

This test was supposed to confirm everything ... at least I hoped so. I was petrified thinking about it and didn't know what to expect. Even though the doctors explained it to me, their medical lingo didn't make much sense.

My dad was there for some of the tests, but he had to return to work. My mom sat with me as often as she could but also had to go to work. On certain testing days, Mom brought work with her; I assume so that she could spend time with me on the scariest days. Sometimes my parents visited after work, and my mom brought me fast food. This was great because the food in the hospital wasn't good, and there were few options for dinner. I'm sure she thought it would make me feel better, and it did. Oddly, though, I don't remember her bringing any snacks. I thought it was strange because she always brought snacks when we went somewhere. The only late-night snack option at the hospital was Jello.

But eventually, my parents had to leave. It was not a good feeling being there day and night all alone. I always wished my parents could stay longer, so I didn't feel so lonely and abandoned. I felt so very isolated and remember wishing they would give me a roommate or that someone else would visit so I could get my mind off of everything. One of the saddest things in the world is a child who is on their own in a hospital room.

Test after test continued, and I wondered what was going to be next. I was only eleven, lying in the hospital most of the time alone and scared out of my mind. Finally, Friday rolled around ... and so did the dreaded muscle biopsy. This was my last hurdle during my hospital stay. I was told they were only going to numb the place where the muscle tissue would be extracted. The first needle went in to deaden the tissue, but I still felt them tugging. Then the second numbing needle came. Yikes! Like any child, I hated needles. But it finally did the trick, and I could no longer feel anything.

However, halfway through the procedure, the medicine started to wear off. So yes, I felt the rest of the biopsy. There are no words to describe the pain other than "excruciating" and "torture." It is still very vivid in my mind today. After that final test, I knew I never wanted to go back into another hospital.

Let's hope that today's methods are much different, for I hate to think of any other kid having to go through that.

***

I was sent home the next day with a pair of crutches but had to stay off my leg for about a week. My bedroom was upstairs, so when I needed something, I banged on the floor with my crutch to signal my mom. Every time I moved, the stitches seemed to pull at the incision. I had thread stitching, and until the tissue got tough enough, I felt the tug on my skin every time I moved! Originally, the wound was probably about one-and-a-half inches long but healed over the years to about a half-inch. I can clearly see, even today, where each stitch went in. Some doctors have mentioned it was a really bad stitching job.

It was probably two weeks before we went back to the neurologist to get the stitches out (those stitches still hurt), and that's when I got the diagnosis. The neurologist determined I had muscular dystrophy, in particular, Charcot Marie Tooth Disease. What an odd-sounding name. We were informed that it was, and still is, a very rare form of muscular dystrophy. There is no cure for it. We could only treat the symptoms with medication and some physical therapy.

Being diagnosed with Charcot Marie Tooth Disease was bad enough, but since I was just a child, it was hard to comprehend what it all meant. Honestly, my parents were probably more shocked than anyone. We were all about to embark on several life lessons within the next few years while dealing with a disability in the family. I never imagined that it would affect my entire life, but it certainly did. It didn't dawn on me that this was serious, and that life as I knew it was about to drastically change… well, the tears started to fall. I was so afraid of what I had to face for the rest of my life, and I just kept crying.

I don't recall what my mom said to me after we received the news. Looking back at it now, I don't remember my parents really talking to me about any of it. I don't even know if my sister was told about it at this point. It seems to me my parents were afraid to talk about it, or maybe I was in shock and just didn't remember them saying anything.

***

From that day onward, it was a whirlwind of learning and absorbing information in order to cope with this muscular and neurological disease, nicknamed CMT. Doctors told us that I could be monitored to see if the symptoms got any worse, but other than that, there was nothing to do but wait. Yes, it was a "wait and see" situation to determine what symptoms might worsen and the strength I might lose in my limbs. Since each individual is affected differently, there was no way to determine how severe my case would be.

My mom finally acknowledged my disease when she went to doctor appointments with me. I don't remember my dad asking me about how I was dealing with everything. I'm just guessing, but I suspect he didn't want any limitations put on me. He always wanted me to be a strong individual. I recall thinking, *Just imagine, after all this time, my aunt's intuition was right.* I look back now and thank her for speaking up on my behalf.

We went to a support group recommended by the neurologist. It was located at the same hospital where I had all the testing done. I was not real happy about that, and my mom took me "kicking and screaming"—I say that figuratively, not literally, for I would not have been allowed to kick and scream. I was simply reluctant and dreaded going.

I looked around the room and saw with my own two eyes just how severe my condition could potentially be. I was trying to understand the ins and outs of a new disease that I had just discovered invaded my body … and then faced a room full of people telling me what they were going through. The more I learned about this disease, the more alarmed I became. Many of the adults shared how tired and weak they had become and how their hands, legs and feet muscles were affected. Then some kids my age showed up, and it was good to know there were others besides me with CMT. They seemed to be further along in their progression.

It was all a bit overwhelming, to say the least. My emotions built up inside, and I wasn't sure whether to scream or cry. The bottom line? I simply didn't believe that a severe degree of disability would actually happen to me. I remember thinking, I'll never go through the same problems as these people. Still, I had never met more challenges than dealing with my neuromuscular disease. I wanted to be strong and not let it bother me, but how could I? What was I supposed to do with my life now? How were things going to change? Question after question reeled in my head, and I felt dizzy and sick.

Although at the time, I didn't think the support groups would benefit me personally, they did benefit my mom. She learned how to address issues with the school and what might come in the future. Little did I know that twenty years later, I, myself, would need the information I learned when I was eleven and twelve. Luckily I retained everything. For instance, I remember a woman in the group who had a hard time cleaning her house but wanted it kept neat. This is exactly what I deal with today. In fact, I mention it in the "Asking for Help" chapter at the end of the book.

At the time, the group sponsor said, "Do a little, and then take a break."

I tried that for a while and was okay, but then it got to be too much once we moved to a bigger home. I then took the group sponsor's second piece of advice:

"Find someone to come in to help you."

I looked at some potential cleaning services online and found someone I could trust. She used to come every other week to help me with the more difficult tasks like vacuuming and bathrooms, as well as other cleaning. When she stopped her cleaning business, I couldn't find a suitable replacement and just tackled housecleaning myself.

Believe it or not, I also learned things that helped me cope much later in my married life, divorced life, dating life, and as a mother. I knew how to talk to my son's teachers so they would understand that his grades shouldn't be lowered due to his handwriting. His gym performance grade shouldn't be based on what he couldn't due, but how hard he tried. I had to talk to his gym teacher, who questioned me. She insinuated that I didn't expose Ryan to "normal" kids so he could learn how to move around. This made me angry; I told her I'd talk to the principal if I had to. By the way, her son was one of the kids who bullied Ryan. It was not a good situation, but thankfully the P.E. teachers rotated. His other gym teacher understood and accommodated Ryan.

My mother took tips and pointers from the group as well. She spoke to my teachers but never let me know about it. I guess she thought I might feel that my teachers would look at me differently or give me special treatment. But all my mother was doing was making them aware of what was causing the problems with the handwriting, etc.

Yes, everything I took away from the group was helpful in one way or another. All of the people in that group set an example. Even listening to everyone's various complaints had a benefit. I learned that I didn't want people to pity me. No, I don't expect people to feel sorry for me for having this disease, but I do want people to have an inkling of what life is like with CMT. Then they'd know what to expect from me or others like me and be comfortable around us.

For example, there have been people who've treated me like I have leprosy—perhaps you have experienced this firsthand if you or a loved one has a disability. I wanted nothing more than to avoid stares, which seemed to be triggered by my abnormal gait and the tremors of my head and hands. Despite my coping skills, to this day, it can be so frustrating! Sometimes I want to tell people: "Take a picture; it will last longer!" Another one I would love to use is: "If you stare long enough, I might do a trick!"

***

Back then, there wasn't a lot of funding from the Muscular Dystrophy Association for this particular form of muscular dystrophy because it is not considered a life-threatening disease. Grant funding is more available now for CMT of all types than there ever was before. Maybe one day, a cure will be found, but then and now, there is still no cure.

By the way, I don't physically attend a CMT support group today, mostly because there isn't one in close proximity to my home. But there are online support groups and social media forums throughout the United States, and even the world. I belong to the Team Inspire group and various Facebook groups that cover CMT topics. Interestingly, a lot of people on the Inspire blog are as frustrated as I am regarding insurance, braces, finding a doctor to help them, what to do about falls, what meds everyone finds helpful depending on the symptoms they are dealing with, and much more. It is really very informative. Many of their comments reflect my thoughts precisely.

There are organizations that try to help provide services at little or no cost to patients with certain diseases. Most of them can be found through the Muscular Dystrophy Association and the Charcot-Marie-Tooth Association. It's amazing the information you can find with just a quick search on your laptop, iPad, or desktop computer. I knew where to locate information for footwear and bracing when I eventually needed them. I know how and where to find resources that help me locate products, as well as research, to help me be my own advocate.

Again, it points back to educating yourself and finding the support you need. It's out there, even for those of us who live with a rare disease. And by all means, I suggest that you take your children to support groups. They may not like it, at least at first, but they will learn from it just as I did. It really will teach them to cope and strategize and navigate their disease.

CHAPTER 3
THE NEW NORMAL

I call horses 'divine mirrors'—they reflect back the emotions you put in. If you put in love and respect and kindness and curiosity, the horse will return that.
~ Allan Hamilton

Kids are generally resilient, and I was no exception. So after the initial shock was over, it was time to move on with my life. In hindsight, horseback riding was the perfect sport for me because I could sit in a saddle while strengthening my leg muscles. It felt like I could walk normally and almost run because of the movement of the horse. But at the time, I rode because I just loved horses.

For a while, it appeared that I might not end up in the saddle after all. You see, I initially took English horse riding lessons when I was very young and learned on "schooling horses." By schooling horses, I mean the kind of horses that are well trained and calm. The horse is the teacher and enables riders to develop new skills. These wonderful creatures give students the confidence to be able to learn and excel.

I eventually went out on a trail ride. After a pretty bad fall on some rocky terrain, I had some minor cuts and was pretty shaken up. I didn't want to get back on a horse. Instead, I took dance lessons, specifically jazz lessons, with a friend for a couple of years. Then the desire to ride horses re-emerged, and I had to go back to the schooling horses for more training. This ensured I was going to stick with it before getting my own pony.

This is where my CMT journey might differ from others, for not everyone gets a pony. I was fortunate that my parents saw the value in horsemanship—the responsibility, the great exercise, and the distinct pleasure of being around such amazing creatures. So, my parents bought me my first pony, Sugar, a Cob pony (a bit larger than a regular pony). She was a sandy-brown color and very cute, with a small heart that had been left on her hindquarters when she had her winter coat shaved off before they bought her for me. Dad's explanation for this purchase was that it would keep me off the street and away from bad influences, not that we had a lot of that in our neighborhood.

Silver Bit and Spur, a stable and riding facility where Sugar was boarded, became my home away from home. I had horse chores, like cooling Sugar down after a ride in the winter, which meant laying a special cooling "blanket" on her back to absorb the heat that accumulated under her saddle. During the summer, I cooled her down by walking her slowly and hosing her off. I picked her hooves and brushed her mane and tail as well. Grooming was my favorite task. These chores taught me responsibility.

Mom sometimes stayed for my lessons but usually dropped me off with trusted instructors. She shopped for hours—sometimes four or five hours—until my group lessons, private lessons and trail rides were over. During the summers, Mom paid for a cab to take me to the barn when she couldn't get away from work and then picked me up after work. Without her willingness to do so, I wouldn't have benefitted from equestrian therapy and the confidence-building shows I competed in.

I have to mention the blind Clydesdale at the stable. He was a gentle giant, and I admired how he handled his disability. One eye was missing, and he couldn't see out of the remaining eye, but his personality was great. He knew the trails so well that he was able to follow them. His blindness didn't affect his ability to work—anyone could ride him. I thought it was great that students could interact with this horse and see that any being, whether human or animal, can make the most of a disability.

Sugar and I enjoyed each other for a few years and even did some shows, but I eventually outgrew her. She became too short for me to jump her without almost going over her neck. My mom and I headed out with my trainer to find a good horse for me. After a little searching, we found a very gentle quarter horse gelding that had to be sold because its owners were divorcing. I'll mention here, tongue in cheek, that this was the best thing that has ever come from a divorce in my experience.

My instructor thought we made a great pair. I remember being a little intimidated by his size, which was just over fifteen hands high. Sugar, in contrast, had been only fourteen hands, which made a huge difference in movement. By "hands," I'm referring to a measurement for a horse. One hand equals four inches, so a horse that measures sixty inches is fifteen hands high. By the way, I still own a measuring tape in hands that was given to me by my vet, and it's come in very handy throughout the years.

This particular horse had bigger movements, but after spending a couple of hours riding and checking out our chemistry, so to speak, my mom made a deal, and he was mine. His papered name was Catoctin Shamrock, but I gave him the barn name Rocky because he rode like a rocking horse once I was used to his canter. We spent whole weekends together, and whenever I was out of school, I was at the barn with him. The warmth of Rocky's body, especially when riding bareback, really helped my back and legs. If we went out for a trail ride, I rode in a western saddle. But the vast majority of the time, I rode English, which was the main riding style on the East coast. I really enjoyed it. I loved the challenge of jumping.

Oh, what a bond we formed. I never imagined it could be possible to have such a great relationship with a horse. It was like he read my mind and anticipated commands and was so smart he'd nod his head as if to say, "Yes, I'd like some," when I offered him a treat.

What followed were many years of English horseback riding. We eventually moved Rocky from Silver Bit to a bigger barn called Pine Hill. My dad called it the "Taj Mahal" since it was a bigger and nicer barn. The trainers had more knowledge and got me to the level I wanted to be at for showing. We did so many shows together that I lost count. In the summers, we did the series at Silver Bit and the Flemington Fair. After showing one month at the fair, I was asked to do a demo before the show started to help people better understand what they were going to see at the horse show. There was also a winter series we did a few times, but it was just too cold to do them all some years.

My final goal was to win the all-around trophy at Silver Bit. That meant I had to be at every show and show in many different classes that we qualified for. In order to do all the classes I needed, my show days went from 6 a.m. to four or five in the afternoon. I liked to wait around long enough to see if I made high point for the day. That would mean I was that much closer to winning the big year-end award.

Back then, I could ride that long without problems. Of course, I had breaks in between some classes and for lunch, so I wasn't on Rocky's back all day long. I'm sure he was thankful for that. After so many shows, he obviously knew the routine and started shaking, trying to make me think he was sick. It scared me to death, but I figured out that he was just trying to get out of a show day, sort of like a kid who fakes an illness to avoid school.

Eventually, I showed in both Western and English as well as halter and trail classes to be able to earn enough points. We did manage to accomplish it by the time I was nineteen and in college. It took a lot of time and training, but I was so proud of myself and Rocky when we achieved it.

I owe a debt of gratitude to my parents, and in particular my mother, for facilitating my interaction with horses. As Winston Churchill once said,

"There is nothing better for the inside of a man than the outside of a horse"—and this truth also applied to a girl who was officially diagnosed with CMT and not wearing braces at the time. Being on a horse still gives me a feeling of stability that I don't have when I am walking. For this reason, I highly recommend horseback riding for people with CMT and other disabilities, especially if they can start early and really adapt to it.

***

My very first job in middle school was at a bakery. I was fourteen and didn't last a full year because my mom got tired of taking me back and forth. After all, she was already putting a lot of mileage on her station wagon when hauling me to the barn and back.

Honestly, my life on horseback made up for a lot of the emotional pain I experienced at school. I followed the regular school routine with the exception of gym class. Thankfully, I was allowed to participate at the level I felt comfortable. I did not have to run hurdles and fall on my face. I did not have to be the last one to come running in from the field. No, I didn't have to worry about things like that anymore and was given leniency for a change. I liked it.

Maybe there are some upsides to this, I thought, although gym class was the only benefit I could see at that point. Again, I was a hopeful young girl with a "glass half full" kind of outlook. It didn't take a lot to make me happy, which is why it was so devastating that some of my peers seemed determined to ruin what happiness I had.

You see, there were the kids who couldn't understand why I was walking differently. They thought it was funny. They thought I was an easy target. Yes, the bullies at my school gave me a hard time, and years later, the same kids would follow me into high school.

"Waddle while you walk," the mean kids said, following behind me and making duck-quacking sounds or pulling chairs out from underneath me. They'd make faces and strange noises, looking me right in the eye while they did it. Or, they'd trip me while walking down the hallway or in class.

There was little-to-no sensitivity training back then. If children had just been made aware of what my disability and other disabilities were about, I think they would have been nicer. I'll never know for sure, though, because that never happened. My teachers didn't seem to stop the mean kids or reprimand them. This is where educating them would have helped.

So, it was up to parents to instill compassion and respect into the minds and hearts of their children. The fact was, some of the kids never received that message. They were so cruel. They'd zero in on someone like me and make life miserable.

This was part of the "new normal" of my formative years. I remember wishing the mean kids could experience what it was like living with CMT for just one day. Then they might understand. Their malevolence made all of the seemingly good things fade away.

Of course, there were kids who felt that the bullying was unfair. They were kind. Thank God I had two best friends who helped "pick back" at the guys who were picking on me. They helped a lot by sticking with me and sitting by me when they could. I did go to some junior high dances with my friends. I remember slow dancing with a boy I had a crush on. He was really sweet to me, no matter what.

These special friendships made life more bearable, but the bullying made it extremely hard to want to go to school. Even with good friends supporting me, the bullying still hurt.

"If you ignore them, they'll go away," I was told, but it didn't go away.

I wanted to punch each one of my tormentors right in the face, as any kid would, but I did my best to deal with it. I knew who to avoid after awhile.

Looking back, I'm so grateful that social media hadn't yet been invented, for that would have been another potential platform for my bullies. If there is one thing I'd like to promote with this book, it's a strong anti-bullying message, whether in school hallways or from behind a keyboard. There's really no excuse for this behavior. It should not be tolerated or condoned.

Being bullied and taunted, of course, can make you a stronger person. That's certainly true in my case. But for some, it's just too painful to bear. That's why even now, in the year 2019, we hear about teens and even young children taking their own lives. They are unable to cope with the humiliation and emotional torture. Sometimes, there's physical abuse, as well, against innocent children who, by no fault of their own, are different or must live with a disability.

I had to adapt to accommodate my shortcomings and learn to cope. But it eventually made me a resilient person. I moved on and was thankful I still had legs that could at least walk. I might never be an Olympian, but I was still getting around, not completely confined to a wheelchair. So, as usual, I counted my blessings.

***

Things didn't change until later in high school. I think some of the boys matured and realized that what they were doing was wrong. Finally, in my sophomore year, I didn't have as many problems. Sure, I still heard the stupid comments, but the chair pulling and tripping had calmed down.

I was involved in several extracurricular activities. For instance, I performed on the flag team for part of my freshman year. I was also in choir from middle school all the way through high school, and sometimes we performed off-campus. I enjoyed being on the diving team and practicing at an off-campus natatorium. I was told the best form of exercise for my type of CMT was swimming. Although the monotonous back and forth laps got boring after a while, it did help with my muscle tone and ankle flexibility.

And then there were driving lessons and obtaining a license—by far one of the most exciting rights of passage for any teen. I was the youngest in my high school class and one of the last to get a driver's license. In New Jersey, the driving age is seventeen. My parents sent me to a driving school, and I also had a driving class at my campus. I drove my Mom's station wagon while I had my permit. After passing my driving test, I drove a Mercury Tracer.

Oh—and I went to both of my proms with two different guys. I was more serious with the one I dated during my junior prom than the one I went with in my senior year. It was a slice of normalcy to date and dance and drive my car. And speaking of normalcy, I'm happy to say my teachers didn't confuse my physical disability with a learning disability. I was bright and earned good grades. I was, and still am, a very capable person.

Again, my dear friend Amy Anderson Gerlach weighs in, this time in with a recap of our high school days below:

Dawn and I navigated high school together. We had boyfriends, we had jobs, and we got in all sorts of trouble—but always together. By this time, Dawn's legs were starting to get weaker, and I noticed her calf muscles almost seemed to be shrinking. During gym class, we were often asked to run around the track. Running required a lot of effort for Dawn, and I was happy to keep her company, so being the rebellious teens that we were, we decided that we preferred to just walk the track. I'm not sure if Dawn chose not to get a "limited ability" diagnosis with the school so that the gym teacher would understand why she chose not to run. I wouldn't be surprised if she didn't, though. She didn't want special treatment or anybody's sympathy.

After some time, though, Dawn did get a doctor's note—I think her mother provided it to the school. Occasionally, Dawn was made fun of and mocked because of the slower way her condition forced her to walk. I remember a group of about four-to-five teenage boys flinging coins at Dawn as she walked past them. It's just what insecure, scared young people do at that age, but at the time, it was terribly painful for Dawn to go through. I remember those moments with a lot of regret for not doing or saying more to stick up for her.

That is a message I want to emphasize over and over again. People may have physical limitations but are still capable of so many things, including loving and helping others with their gifts and talents. But the downside to limitations is also very real and causes us to endure the cruelty that others sometimes display. People with handicaps are generally very strong mentally and emotionally for this reason—we have to be.

Relaxing between classes

Winning first place in a halter class

Horse kisses are the best!

Finally won the all around year end trophy! Goal accomplished.

Flemington Fair Show

CHAPTER 4
LESSONS ON COPING

There is a story behind every person.
There is a reason why they are the way they are.
Think about that, and respect them for who they are.
~ Marcandangel

The bullying I endured wasn't pleasant, but it does lead to some important topics, namely the correlation between limitations and self-esteem. They do go hand in hand. Having limitations takes a physical, emotional, and social toll.

I do believe I would have been a very good athlete if it weren't for CMT. I wanted to try out for the Olympics for jumping and endurance riding. I knew if I had the legs of a "normal person," I could go all the way. What a wonderful dream to aim for, if only reality fit the dream.

I think my father never realized that I had those aspirations. As a child, my horseback riding was never good enough. I very rarely remember getting a nice comment when he watched me perform at a horse show. Rather than inspiring me to do better, his words only made me feel worse, because I knew I had done my absolute best. It really made me ask myself, *Why is he trying to tell me what to do when he has never ridden English a day in his life or jumped a horse?* I know that he wanted me to do well, but I just wanted to hear "That was great" or "I'm so proud of you." After all, I accomplished so much while battling a disease.

Yes, his harshness made me the person I am today. It did some good by making me strong. But it definitely affected me psychologically, and I still never think what I do is good enough despite my wholehearted efforts. My self-esteem was destroyed in childhood, and today I am still working through the scenarios from my past.

Long story short, I was always given all the material things that I needed but never received all the emotional necessities from my father. A person dealing with CMT needs compassion and reassurance, and having been ridiculed many times, it made it very difficult for me to believe in myself. I just wanted to please my father like any daughter, and my failure to live up to his expectations stung.

Certainly, the fact that my father was unable to accept me for who I was and what I accomplished put a wall between us. I hope that one day that wall will be torn down. If there is one piece of advice I'd give any family with a disabled loved one, it's to be kind, patient, and supportive. Build people up rather than tear them down. Mind your words, for hearts are fragile, and the tongue is the strongest muscle in the body.

Thankfully, I now know that my Father above in heaven loves me and always will, no matter what. I realize that my earthly dad had a rough childhood, which made it difficult for him to deal with me compassionately. That was all he knew, and I forgive him for the past, but will never forget how hard I had to work, and still have to work, to get past all of the psychological issues he created within me.

My mom has been a huge help. She showed me compassion and understanding when my dad was extremely tough on me. I don't think I could have made it through to adulthood without becoming completely crazy if it wasn't for our special relationship. We were very close, and she was there for almost every doctor's appointment or hospital stay. To this day, we try to maintain a close relationship. She stays busy, but if I need help with something, she tries to be there. She was, and is, my guardian angel as well as my mom.

***

I was tempted at times to let the situation get the best of me, but instead mastered a very important life lesson. In order to maintain a healthy dose of self-esteem despite my limitations, I had to learn how to cope. Yes, I had to cope with my family dynamics and also my disease. So how did I handle CMT, and how can others do the same when faced with daunting adversity?

First, I had to get past the humiliation of my circumstances. One of my tougher challenges was, and still is, falling. I never know when I was going to trip or fall. Imagine what it was like to feel good about yourself one minute, and the next minute experience such embarrassment. Yep. I'd be stumbling and wobbling or down on the ground, asking once again, *Why me? Why should I have to be in this position, fleeling embarrassed? Why are you doing this to me, God? Why do I deserve this?*

It ruined my day. It hurt my pride. After all, whether you are a teen or an adult, you worry a lot about what others are thinking. I wish more people had offered a hand instead of a weird glare! Then I'd calm down, stop for a minute to regroup, get up, brush myself off, and keep on going. I had such a strong desire to beat the disease. It wasn't just willpower, though, that helped me keep going. It was faith.

I wasn't brought up in a religious home, but I did go to church with my aunt in Texas during the summers. When I was a teenager, I was involved with my sister's youth group. I started seeing things a little more clearly and developed the faith I so desperately needed.

I learned that God must have some sort of plan for me. Whatever it was, I was brought along this certain path to learn about Him. He obviously wanted me to be a strong person, considering my circumstances, and perhaps my ordeal was meant to be a testimony for others going through tough times.

Still, obviously, my faith was tested. Many times I wanted to give up on God and my beliefs because of the hand I had been dealt. Sometimes it felt like I was the only one going through this, but I knew deep down that I was not alone. Many people were dealing with much more than a nonfatal neuromuscular disease. There were plenty of fatal conditions that could have invaded my body. Yes, plenty of other people faced terrible trials, which made mine pale in comparison.

So I learned to count my blessings, and in a strange way, became thankful. This was, and is, a wonderful coping mechanism, but believe me, it was not always easy to be thankful. After all, my loved ones watched me go through the struggles and suffered along with me. They didn't always know what to do to make me feel better. It was so comforting when they hugged me and wiped my tears and let me know I was still loved.

I would think, God loves me too, and that's what matters. I'd try to forget about the hardships and move on to the next thing. And then I'd trip and fall again, and the pain from whatever body part I had fallen on would remind me again of my plight. Sometimes I found myself getting angry at God because of what I was going through. Over time, I learned that was the wrong way to think of things.

I eventually learned not to worry so much about what others saw. The sooner I focused my thinking on what God saw—me, his own creation—the easier it became. That's the key. Yes, faith in God helped my self-esteem. It got me through each day, then and now. It's a very important way of thinking in order to move past these embarrassing and painful moments.

Once I realized God was by my side every day, I knew I was going to persevere while dealing with CMT. Honestly, my coping skills were strengthened when I reminded myself that God is in control and that there are rhyme and reason to my circumstances. This truth kept me grounded about the real issues at hand. And without Him in my life, I would already have lost it. To this day, He is my strength and inspiration while making it through my complicated condition.

***

Looking back, another challenging aspect of life was all the doctor appointments. Even now, the medical aspects still disrupt my life. I can either complain about it or pray about it and take it in stride. For example, before the diagnosis, I only went to a pediatrician. After the diagnosis, it was a whole new ballgame. I had to see neurologists, chiropractors, orthopedists, etc., and still do. It seemed like I was always pulled out of school and missing time in the classroom. My parents had to let the administration and teachers know what was going on. Of course, I had doctor's excuses to cover the absences, but what I got out of all this was a sense of teamwork. People worked together on my behalf and in my best interests.

Today I work as an administrative assistant at WFI, a family-owned business. So, it's not class I'm missing, but rather time at my job. Just as the school required details about my condition and why my absences were necessary, I keep my folks apprised of whatever treatment or appointment I face. Honestly, I don't want to always report everything. Sometimes I'd just like to take the afternoon off for an appointment without having to describe the details. But this, too, is part of coping, especially when working in a family business. It's important to let those around you know of your circumstances.

Speaking of doctors, many people have issues trusting doctors. I never really understood why, until it happened to me. It circles back to the wheelchair and the assurances that I would never need one. Well, it turns out, the doctors were wrong. The year my power chair was dropped off at my house, I realized that doctors—or anyone, for that matter—are not omniscient. They can't tell the future, no matter what kind of tests are run. They could not have ever known whether I would need a wheelchair or not. Perhaps they were just trying to comfort me, but the fact is, a wheelchair sits in my garage.

I couldn't believe it myself—me, who still rode horses and taught riding lessons—suddenly needed the help of a wheelchair. Still, I was determined not to let it take over my life. It never has and never will. This sense of optimism and resiliency also helps me cope. Today I use a scooter to move around in the yard to avoid the risk of falling, but in the house and on the smoother pavement, I'm still walking with my own two legs. That, my friends, is a blessing, although I use a cane or a walker if I'm not wearing braces.

I now question everything. Yes, that is part of coping as well. I'm the type who likes to look at every medical angle and get second opinions. If my neurologist says one thing, I check it out with my regular physician, and vice versa. You have to be an advocate for yourself. You can regain some sense of control by learning self-advocacy skills. I learned to ask questions and get the facts. I became a student of my disease and learned as much about my complicated condition as possible.

***

And speaking of complicated conditions, having a son with a disability nearly identical to mine prompted me to raise him with a mindset of optimism, resiliency, gratitude, and thankfulness. Yes, I raised Ryan in church, and he developed his own sense of faith. He faced childhood trials as I had, but with the gentle reminder of one of my favorite sayings: If God brings us to it, He will bring us through it.

These words made all the difference and equipped Ryan to cope. It equipped him for the afterlife as well, I believe. Life can be so fleeting. As I grapple with losing him so unexpectedly at such a young age, I constantly ask why. Why was my son taken from me? Why him and not me? He had his whole life before him. But even in my questioning state, I continue to look up to God for grace, hope and guidance.

It brings to mind the comforting words in a book entitled Powerful Prayers for Women written by Janice Deal and Marie Jones:

"God of comfort, help me lift my eyes and look beyond myself.

What people around me are in need of your consolation?

Have you given this difficult experience to equip me to help them?

Are there other ailing people who will listen to me because I know what they're going through? Are there people visiting me who are troubled by worries and fears?

Are there doctors and nurses who are overworked and

desperately need a moment of joy or a word of love?

Show me these needs and how I can see them."

CHAPTER 5
INTO ADULTHOOD

Courage does not always roar.
Sometimes courage is the quiet voice at the end of the day saying, 'I will try again tomorrow.'
~ Mary Anne Radmacher

Have I mentioned that I never thought it would take so many doctors to take care of one person with a neuromuscular disease? I went from just a pediatrician to a neurologist, podiatrist, chiropractor, a doctor at the Muscular Dystrophy Association clinic, and a movement disorder clinic located within a hospital. These doctors, together, helped me stay as comfortable as possible and also kept track of the progression of my disease, as well as my strength. The neurologist checked all of my reflexes at each appointment and all of the strength and weakness in my face, legs, hands and arms as well.

I remember my first neurologist used to make me pucker up, "Like I was kissing a boy," he would say, to check my facial reflexes. So as time went on, I realized that CMT could also affect facial features and speech as well in certain people. All of this was to make sure the disease wasn't progressing, and for some reason, my upper body strength received good reports, while my lower body became weaker as time went by.

Having a chiropractor appointment three times a week over a long period of time can certainly put a dent in a girl's social schedule. I needed these appointments to keep my hips and back in line due to the way I was walking. Sometimes those appointments took as little as fifteen-to-twenty minutes, but at other times took an hour—not something a teenage girl wants to do. I simply had to for the benefits my body received from the adjustments. In hindsight, I believe it prepared me for life as an adult with CMT and the self-care, not to mention the professional care that was required.

I wasn't allowed to work in high school, as my parents wanted me to focus on my studies and extracurriculars. I began applying for college in my junior year of high school. I thought about applying to a college in Virginia school for equestrian studies, but it was too expensive. Plus, I had to be in the state of New Jersey in order to stay close to Rocky, my horse. Then I considered a two-year business college, but my parents (especially my dad) insisted I attend a four-year college and pursue a degree in business.

I graduated high school in a cap and gown on stage in 1989, and started college that same year. I was accepted at Rider University and earned that four-year degree in three and a half years by taking a lot of summer courses. The fact that I wasn't allowed to work in college (again, my parents wanted me to focus on my studies) probably helped to expedite my speedy path to graduation. My major was business administration, and I joined a co-ed business fraternity, but I concentrated on marketing and advertising as much as possible. I should have switched to an advertising school halfway through, but I just wanted to graduate as quickly as possible.

I don't remember my college peers being rude about my problems. A few people I didn't know looked at me funny, but I was fairly high functioning. I did have friends and a few different boyfriends that I dated at different times, one on campus and others back home. Initially, I shared a dorm room with a roommate as a freshman. We weren't compatible and didn't share the same value system. So the next year, I requested a room that was handicap-friendly. It was a lot nicer and allowed me to live by myself, which was great because I didn't have to share a bathroom or endure a culture clash with a roommate.

The campus had some handicap features, but not many. There was only one handicap parking spot near my dorm located about a block and a half away. I did laundry downstairs in my dorm and took the stairs to get to class. I carried all my books and found it more of a challenge when I had classes back-to-back in different buildings. But I did manage to arrive on time, or made it just as they were closing the doors.

By the way, my campus was considered a "suitcase college" because there were so many commuters and students who lived at home. Plus, almost all of my peers went home on weekends—including me. My weekends were devoted to spending time with my horse and training for my next competition. Normally, after practice, I had studying to do. As a member of the Rider Equestrian Team, considered a college group, I earned a jacket during my first two years. I was proud of that accomplishment, mainly because we had to ride different horses with different attitudes. We picked out of a hat and never knew what kind of horse we'd be riding.

There was a pool on my college campus that I used during the week. I also went to a YMCA when I had downtime on the weekends when I wasn't working with the horses. The only time I stayed on campus was if I was dating someone there. We did have semi-formal dances, and I think I went to at least two, both with different guys. I enjoyed every minute of it! I also enjoyed walking the stage at my college graduation ceremony in cap and gown, but remember being more afraid of falling in college because of the size of the stage and the number of stairs.

After graduating, I started to teach horseback riding to clients. I first did some private lessons on the schooling horses at Silver Bit, and then started to travel to people who had their own horses and wanted to learn certain things on horseback. It was so much fun being able to teach people what I loved to do.

Teaching riding lessons was a wonderful way to share the joy of horses with others and stay fit. My kind companion, Rocky, started doing therapeutic lessons once we moved to Texas. He showed many students the wonderful sport of riding. Whether English, Western or therapeutic lessons, he never complained and gave his nice easy walking gait to all of those who rode on his back. He let them ride backward, standing up, lying down, or whatever needed to be done. He just went right along with it.

One disabled student came to me after surviving a series of seizures. His mother was terrified of horses but brought him to therapeutic lessons. When he first started with me, he was very rigid and stiff. His mom's number one complaint was that she had a hard time opening his legs to diaper him. We did stretching of all sorts, including stretching to the ears with a side walker's help and me riding behind him, holding his waist. These were exercises he couldn't do on his own. He got to a point where he started vocalizing, and I could tell he understood what was going on. It made him excited. His mom finally told me after a couple of months that she had the first experience of putting a diaper on him without having to fight to get his legs open. This was proof that the exercises were working.

I always put him on a bareback pad rather than a saddle because the warmth helped his legs and entire body. At the end of his lesson, I got off the horse and turned the boy around to face Rocky's rear, with a sidewalk positioned at his hands and feet to keep him stable. I put another pad down and laid him down backward to get a different stretch in his arms and legs. I kept watch to make sure his head didn't bob to one side or the other. Also, I took Rocky to one of his birthday parties. I thought that was really neat, and Rocky gave all the kids rides.

***

If there is one thing that really bugs me, it's handicap parking. It is supposed to be a good thing for anyone who needs to use it, provided they have the placard or license plate to park in one. But using the space sometimes had consequences for someone like me. What I have found over the years is if the top half of you looks normal, you might get nasty looks for parking in a handicap spot. Apparently, you are supposed to be deformed or handicapped all over your body in order to park in one. Yes, I am young to be parking in a handicap spot, but who put an age limit on disease and disability? I did not use these spots until after the age of eighteen or even older, and I displayed the appropriate placard, but apparently, I should have been gray-headed or hunched over in my car before pulling into a handicap parking space.

I cannot tell you how many people have approached me or have said something in passing about me not parking there because I was not handicapped. It's only when I exit my car and start to walk that people notice that there is something wrong. Honestly, it is not for them to judge. This is one subject that is a personal sore spot. Of course, all of the idiots who use their spouse's, relative's or friend's placard just to get a closer space have made it harder for people like me and all the other people who really need a reserved spot.

Once while I was still living in New Jersey, a man started yelling at me in the parking lot. He told me I should not be parking in a spot made for the "disabled," and it didn't matter to him that I had the proper placard in place. I proceeded to follow him into the store and caught up with him when he stopped at the pharmacy counter.

He turned around and said, "How dare you park in a handicap spot when you are normal."

I lit a fire under him in front of all the people standing there and had him tongue-tied.

"If I did not have the awful disease of muscular dystrophy, then I would not need that spot. Just because I look normal on my upper body does not mean that the bottom half is functioning all that well. My inside nervous system feels like a wreck," I announced.

There was dead silence in that store. I made my point, and he didn't know what to say. I went about my shopping, and he never bothered me again. Neither did anyone else in the store. Things like that make me so angry. It is irritating for idiots like that to try and tell a person whether they should or should not be parking in a handicapped spot. I hope he will never forget me, and I'm sure he won't.

It seems the more things change, the more things stay the same. Just recently, I was at the grocery store and had a hard time finding a handicap parking space. My usual spot right next to the door had a truck parked across all three spaces! This meant I had further to walk on an unusually windy day.

The gusts made walking toward the entrance quite difficult.

A guy approached me and said, "Are you okay, baby?" He didn't realize there was a medical condition involved, although it had to be fairly obvious.

I said, "Yes, of course," but what I really wanted to say is: "There is only one person who calls me baby, and that's my husband." However, I was nice and continued into the store, still having a hard time walking.

I was feeling angry about the handicap parking issue as I picked up the few items I needed and told the supervisor about it. It turns out, they normally had police surveillance, but not on that day. The supervisor said she'd try to get the situation taken care of, although the parking offender had already left. It goes to prove, one more time, that people need to be more informed.

Today if I see someone pulling into a handicap spot without a placard or plate, I approach them and/or call the authorities. If someone has the audacity to park in a handicap spot simply to get closer to a store entrance, then they are lazy and inconsiderate and ruin it for those of us who really need the spaces. It's just plain rude and selfish! I had a sheriff's office willing to participate in catching some of these people. They gave the number to call and report the license plate number and where they were parked, but never came to enforce the law. How will things ever get better if the law isn't enforced?

Okay, I will now step off my soapbox, but hopefully, some of these insights will encourage people to do the right thing and not park in a handicap space unless they have a disability. Also, I hope it inspires people with disabilities to stand up for themselves in these awkward situations.

One of Rocky's professional photos taken before he started getting old.

CHAPTER 6
ANKLE-FOOT ORTHOSIS

The greater the obstacle, the more glory in overcoming it.
~ Moliere

Here's an interesting bit of trivia. Some high-profile people who have CMT include Julie Newmar, who starred for two seasons as Catwoman in the 1960s television series "Batman." Anthony Ramos, a Los Angeles comedian, talks about CMT in his act. Paralympian Anthony Zahn has CMT and trained hard to become a bronze medalist. I bet each one of them can tell personal stories about footcare, bracing, surgery and pain management. It's all a part of living with CMT.

The podiatrist certainly played a huge part in my high school years because I sprained my ankles frequently and spent a lot of time in air casts, which simply encase an ankle in a cushioned casing to reduce pain and promote healing. Finally, I found that high top sneakers solved my ankle problems for awhile. It made dressing up and going out challenging. All I wanted to make sure of was that I was never looked at as someone with CMT.

The truth is, however, that CMT is a progressive disease, which means it becomes more debilitating, not to mention noticeable, as people age. It drastically affects our ability to walk. Opening up and discussing the very real issues I deal with is uncomfortable. It is not in my nature to complain. I'm much more the "overcomer" type of person and don't want to come across as a Debbie Downer or a Negative Nancy. But my mission is to spread awareness about CMT and educate people about the havoc it causes behind the scenes.

Frankly, it's important to speak out for myself and the 1 in every 2,500 people in the United States who are affected and need to wear braces. I was eventually fitted with Ankle-Foot Orthosis, or AFOs. Not everyone with Muscular Dystrophy will have to experience AFOs, but the lucky ones with a dropped foot, weak ankles, or weak calves or thighs will have the pleasure of wearing them! In my case, I had all of the above.

First, I wore high top shoes, either sneakers or boots, so I could have ankle support. I also had the air braces, as I mentioned, for instances when I frequently sprained my ankle because they were so weak. Once I was in college, though, I was given an insert for my shoe that kept me from walking on the outside of my foot and helped support my instep and ankle.

I avoided wearing actual AFOs until I was in my late twenties. They weren't so bad at first and gave me a lot of lower leg support. That's where I am the weakest, and I always wear them if I have to work outside. They aren't the most eye-pleasing thing to wear, so when people stare at me, I've gotten to the point that I just stare back. They eventually look away or just ask what the braces are for. I would rather inform people, honestly, so that society realizes that some people need a little extra help and support while walking.

AFOs for anyone are uncomfortable and a nuisance, but the payoff is worth it when you can almost walk like a normal person—and drive like a normal person. Now that I'm getting older, it is harder to drive some days because of my braces or pain, and I know I'll miss it terribly once I'm unable to drive a typical car. However, I will have my vehicle adapted with hand controls or purchase a van that is totally accessible and equipped for wheelchairs.

When I'm in plastic all day, my legs are colder in the winter, but hotter in the summer (which is preferable due to my legs feeling cold all the time). After all, plastic doesn't breathe well. Interestingly, that plastic has to be custom made for me. If you ever need to have AFOs made for you, it's good to be aware of what goes into getting a pair. First, you have to be measured so an exact cast of your leg and foot can be made. The specialist puts a warm wrap over rubber tubing around your leg where you need the brace. Then it is rubbed with warm water, which feels really good to me. After a few minutes, it dries and is cut off. The rubber tubing, by the way, protects your leg during this process.

Then you wait for the actual brace to be made and return to the specialist to be fitted in them. Most times, they are too long and too big, but are adjusted to fit you just right. After wearing them for a week or two, you'll probably have to go back in because they start rubbing somewhere, and you'll need another adjustment.

If your body ever changes in the slightest (growth, weight gain, injury, muscle atrophy, etc.), then so will your legs and feet. This makes it painful sometimes to wear the braces that once fit you. So there are frequent visits back to the prosthetics doctor to readjust them. In other words, AFOs are a great product when all is said and done, but it may take a while to have a comfortable pair.

Without braces, I'm so clumsy that I sometimes don't feel like walking at all. I usually don't wear braces around the house and instead hold onto furniture or use canes and walkers because my balance is so bad. Wearing braces out in public makes me feel more stable but still does not correct my walking gait altogether. Sometimes I get looks from people like I'm an alien, and other times there are nice people who want to help. Wearing these high plastic things on your legs does tend to draw attention!

People could just simply ask what they are and how the braces help, but instead, they stare and glare. Again, society is so unaware of all the problems people might have to go through just to get around. I think there should be an etiquette class required in school that teaches students about the struggles of people with physical handicaps. Not everyone accomplishes things in the same way, and that is okay. People with disabilities are people too.

Oh—and if you are a female with CMT, it makes it hard to dress up in glamorous shoes. You either feel like they are going to fall off or they don't have enough support. I have to buy dress shoes that are two to three times my normal size to accommodate the brace, but they never are wide enough to fit my braces at all. I know my son had a hard time with the brace rubbing through his jeans. He also had a hard time finding a wider width in shoes or tough enough material to accommodate the brace. We both hated shoe shopping for this reason.

On top of that, some pant legs don't fit easily over the AFO, or the pant leg sticks to the AFO. I'm constantly adjusting the bottom of my pants, and I'm sure the males with CMT have some of the similar problems.

It's important to mention that insurance doesn't always cover the cost of AFOs, and they aren't cheap. If you are fortunate and your policy covers them, the insurance companies expect you to fit in them for a while. They normally won't approve another pair unless it has been a few years. Yet as I mentioned, not every person stays the same, and most cannot fit in a single pair for that long.

In August of 2010, I had a new pair of AFOs made after being fortunate enough to wear the old pair for ten years. The prosthetics specialist told me during the adjustment that the AFOs no longer fit me correctly. I had gone in to get the right brace fixed to make it more comfortable, and I showed the prosthetic specialist where it was hurting. She agreed with the podiatrist that wearing the AFOs in the house might help with the pain in my right foot and help avoid surgery.

The new set was made differently, so the pressure was kept off of the right side of my foot. The whole goal, really, was to put an end to my pain. I had to gradually work up to wearing a brace that high. It required that I start slowly—a half hour or so a day—and then increasing the length of time every other day.

The new AFOs still enabled me to drive a car, which is a good thing. I just had to get used to driving all over again in new braces. The "break-in" period, as I call it, is the hardest part. My feet get numb, and sores appear on my ankles. I normally end up going back a few times for adjustments just for my ankles. Once they fit correctly, I can tolerate them longer. Unfortunately, this process is inevitable when getting new AFOs unless you are lucky enough to have them fit right the first time around. I have heard that it is rare and I've never experienced it myself. But then my left leg bothered me, and I was told I was in the best possible brace unless I want one to go up over my thigh. I just wasn't ready for that.

Dynamic Braces

Finally, I was fitted for a DynamicBracingSolutions™ AFO that deals with complex pathomechanical profiles and can help with issues like my high steppage gait, walking balance, tripping over my feet, ankles that rollover or even my knees buckling.

Dynamic Braces are one of the newest types of braces and are supposed to help me walk more normally and not on my heels. That correction is something I have never experienced in my last two sets of braces. It takes about three months to have them made, and then I had to spend two days in Austin where the specialist, Jason Jennings, is located. He serves a variety of patients—post-polio, CMT, stroke, TBI, peripheral nerve injuries, spina bifida, foot/ankle limb salvage, and lower limb amputees. He's an encyclopedia when it comes to knowledge about fitting people with disabilities, especially CMT. Unfortunately, my insurance didn't help much with the cost, and it is a big expense. If it weren't for my parents, I wouldn't have been able to get the braces. I'm so grateful that they could help, and if it works, it will be well worth it.

Jason taught me how to use the braces. Showing me how to make them work was one thing, but it was up to me to learn how to walk in them. Even after six months, I was still learning to walk correctly and assume this will be an ongoing struggle. Jason said it takes about ten thousand correct steps for a body to learn the technique. I was told I'd be able to depend on these braces more than any other type of brace used previously and that my balance should improve drastically. My balance is good, but walking and balancing at the same time is still a challenge. I was really excited about the braces and hoped they work as described. So far, so good. I'm still taking baby steps to learn how to balance correctly and walk in a whole new way. It takes a lot of practice, including the exercises that were given to me.

I spoke to another lady who has a different type of CMT, and she confirmed the difference is "night and day." So far, I'm not getting the same result but was told I was weaker than her. One recent Saturday, my head burst open as I fell coming through the garage entry to my house while making my way to the kitchen. I was wearing my new braces while carrying groceries, and my head connected with the cabinet and slid all the way down.

Fortunately, my brother was next door and took me to the emergency room at eight in the evening. Around midnight, I got two staples in my head with no anesthesia. They didn't even bring me Tylenol. Finally, we got out of there around 2:30 a.m.

I reported this to the brace specialist, Jason Jennings, and he informed me that it could take a year or more to get used to my new braces.

"Jason," I said to him, "you don't understand. I really cannot walk in these things!"

"I told you I'd make you mad by the time you'd worn them a while!" he responded, although he admitted he had never had to use braces. If he did, he'd probably have problems too. Then he told me to keep doing the exercises.

He was right—I was mad that the braces made walking and balancing so difficult. In my case, they seemed to make me even more accident-prone. They were definitely not the magic bullet I had hoped for, but perhaps I will get used to them. It is getting easier, but some days I want to throw them.

On my last brace appointment, Jason adjusted the braces and gave me more instructions on how to balance and walk. And then he told me I might never walk correctly in the braces due to my muscle weakness. That was news to me—"failure" had never been mentioned before. I was feeling pretty worried and frustrated because of the time, energy and money that had been invested in the braces. Only time will tell whether the braces work or not.

Perhaps I am simply wearing out, for I fell again while wearing the braces. This time I didn't hit my head, and I'm honestly not sure how I ended up on the floor. I fell on my bad hip again, with poor Dixie jumping up and down. I was screaming in pain, and it upset her. But I managed to get up, stretch, reassure the dog, and keep going. I have to remember, too, that CMT is a progressive disease, and this is my progression. I am living the definition. Everyone has a different progression manifesting in the hands, feet, or legs, depending on the form of CMT or MD.

I, personally, have many friends who are on antidepressants to help them "do life," and I am no exception. They help me keep on keeping on. Lately, there are days I just want to sit and do nothing, but my job is to sit at a computer and do something. I have to keep going forward and be as mobile as possible. Thank God I can still drive, although it is getting harder to do so.

I can't help but mention one of my favorite photos in which Ryan and I are both wearing our braces. They weren't matching braces (mine were clear, and his were in camouflage), but just the fact we both wore them made it feel like "twinning." The grins on our faces say it all. We knew we were different and set apart from the rest of the population, but to us, it was just part of everyday life. Think about it—it's rare to meet others with the same rare disease, so the fact that Ryan and I had each other made living with CMT more bearable, and sometimes even fun! If you could see Ryan's contagious smile, you'd know what I mean.

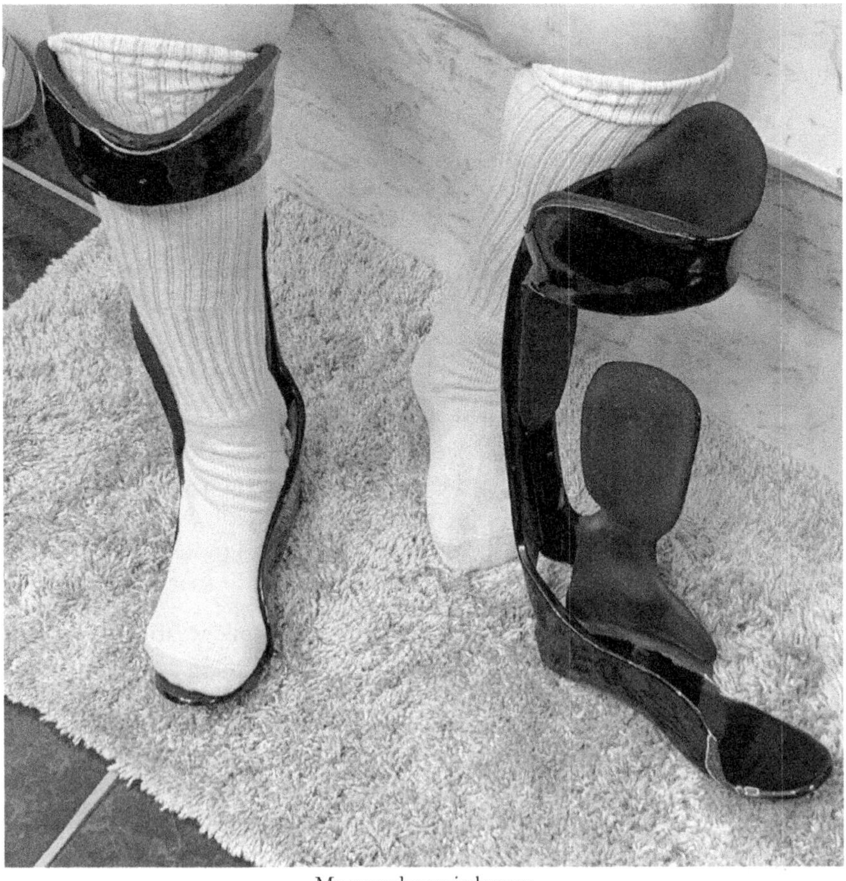

My new dynamic braces

Ryan and me wearing our AFOs

CHAPTER 7
TEXAS

I wasn't born in Texas, but I got here as fast as I could!
~ Popular quip about the Lone Star State

I graduated from college in 1993 and worked at Forbes Newspaper in New Jersey for nearly two years before they closed down. It was a great job, and we had a lot of fun. I worked in the classified section and enjoyed the staff "contests." The guy I dated worked in the layout division. We went riding on Harley motorcycles quite often. His friend took care of the fleet of Forbes motorcycles, and we had free access to them unless the owner was using them.

So, how did I end up living in the Lone Star state? Well, my parents moved to East Texas during the last semester of my senior year in college to take care of my grandfather. But honestly, I moved south because I was heartbroken over the guy I dated at Forbes. We lived in the same town and worked at the same place, and I thought he was going to propose. Instead, he broke it off and moved away. My best friend was wrapped up in her boyfriend, and my cousin had married his new wife, so I felt I had no one.

I initially planned to locate near Corpus Christi, where English riding was much more prevalent. I would have also been closer to my aunt. My parents, however, wanted me to give East Texas a try, and so I did. Much to my surprise, I met my first husband within the second day I was here. That is a story unto itself, as you'll see.

But first, my best friend Amy Anderson Gerlach reflects on this "big move" to the Lone Star State:

Dawn's parents decided to move to Texas. Dawn's father is originally from the East Texas area. After Dawn graduated and had a job for a few years, she realized that although the New Jersey winters aren't very extreme, the cold weather was causing her muscles and joints to ache. She decided to move to Texas to be closer to her family and to help alleviate pain from the colder weather. Dawn packed up her apartment and arranged to have Rocky brought to Texas too—there was no way she was leaving him behind!

I, of course, agreed to drive out to Texas with her. It was a fun road trip. We stopped at the Natural Bridge State Park in Virginia, and after a long day of driving, we also stopped at a local bar that was by our hotel. I joked with Dawn that if any guys hit on us, we'd call ourselves Thelma and Louise, just like the movie.

When we did make it to Texas, I learned that Dawn's new address would be Douglass, which isn't far from Nacogdoches—the oldest town in Texas. It was a bit of a culture shock for me; I surely wasn't used to people being friendly and considerate! One night, Dawn and I ventured out to one of the local watering holes called Jitterbugs. It was a cavernous building with a couple of bars on the perimeters. Why was it so big? For line dancing! We had a couple of cowboys ask us to dance, and soon we were twirling around the huge dance floor. Dawn was doing her best and in her honest, upfront way explained right from the beginning that she would need her partner to be patient because of her legs. And none of the cowboys who asked her to dance had a problem with that. Dawn's beautiful blonde curls, pretty blue eyes and cute curves were all that they noticed!

With a heavy heart, I left my best friend in Texas and flew home to New Jersey. We made a pact that we would talk on the phone once a week, and for a good long time, we stuck to that schedule. That is how we kept up with each other's lives.

***

So, I came to Texas for horseback riding opportunities and began to build my business from the ground up. My teaching career took off, and I offered riding lessons in a round pen out in the middle of a horse field. Actually, we had two pens—one for riding and one for lunging.

We'd free lunge the horses by making them move around us with certain commands. It helped the horse and rider stay in tune with one another. It earned the horse's respect—not only should lunging be physical exercise, but mental exercise as well.

I was able to offer people lessons on my own horse, or if they owned a horse, they could ride it instead of using mine. I taught from the ground up, meaning students learned how to take care of the horse—brushing, saddling, and cooling them out after riding.

Eventually, my parents built a riding arena that protected us from the weather. That's when we used the lunge line by attaching a rope and moving the horse around me. It helps the students learn the basics of riding without worrying about steering, especially while doing the exercises. It's a beneficial exercise for both student and their horses. When lunging the horse before the lesson, it allows the horse to work off energy before it is ridden.

I rode with my students only if they were too young to understand the instructions or if their disability prevented them from following instructions. Then I was able to offer my students therapeutic riding, which involved quite a few regulatory requirements. I did hours of observing therapeutic lessons near Longview. Once I had earned enough hours, I had a lesson recorded as I taught it. This had to be sent in for evaluation, along with all of my lesson preparation per NARHA requirements (now called PATH). I also had to pass a written examination to qualify me for certification as a therapeutic riding instructor.

For those unfamiliar with therapy horses, I want to share their amazing value as companions, teachers, encouragers and facilitators. They are truly another means through which God blesses us. Thanks to these noble creatures, children who could not speak suddenly find their voices. Children who could not walk take their first steps. Some who feared animals form a trust bond that only horses can achieve. It truly is humbling to witness these life-changing interactions firsthand, and it makes me feel grateful that working with horses has been my calling.

Therapeutic riding helped me, as well. I began to stretch on my horse as I learned about therapeutic techniques. The stretches helped my whole body. One of my favorites involved laying down bareback or in an English saddle and reaching for the horse's ears. I had my students do the stretches as well. It was incorporated into everyone's lessons, but the students who stretched the most were beginners and those who came for therapy sessions, as well as the men I taught. Men have a tendency to "hunch" and have to learn how to sit up and back.

I'd also twist from side to side with my arms out or do circles for upper body strength and to loosen up my shoulders. In another type of stretch, we stood straight up in the stirrups with our heels down, so our calves did the work. With disabled students, I had side walkers who helped the students stand up. Eventually, most students could stand in stirrups without assistance, and even if it was for a second, we considered it such an accomplishment!

In short, it's awesome what the outside of a horse can do for the human body.

Just as the schooling horses of my youth helped me decide if I wanted a lifelong relationship with horses, it was the same for my students. I've mentored three who still ride today and are successful. One rides and competes on a college team with a "great seat," meaning the way she sits in the saddle. She's always one of the top winners, whether that's first, second or third. Another wins quite a lot of money performing in rodeos. The third was homeschooled and helped me with therapeutic lessons, which brought her out of her shell and enabled her to be more open with other human beings. It also improved her schoolwork. She helped around the barn to earn her lessons. Now she's a successful trainer and competitor.

I began wearing high top riding sneakers when they became available. I rode in them and taught horseback riding in them before I needed ankle-foot orthoses, or AFOs. In my mid-thirties, the riding was undertaken in moderation. If I taught one day and wanted to ride as well, it was too much for my body, especially due to the bursitis in my hips. My heart said do it, but my joints just couldn't take much exertion anymore. It is such a letdown, for there was nothing better than being in the barn and/or riding. That had always been, and remains, my dream.

My falls in the arena increased because the dirt was so thick and uneven as I walked through it. I was sometimes afraid of breaking something. I loved being with the horses and working with people, and remember thinking, *I love what I do; I just wish it did not attack my body so badly. I'm not even on the back of a horse most of the time when I hit the ground!*

I know, pretty funny, right? I didn't think I would ever admit that my legs got so weak and tired that I just fell down. But I also thought, *This disease will not defeat me. I won't let it as long as I am still breathing.* I may be a glutton for punishment, but I have always fought hard to make sure that CMT didn't take over.

So I kept getting back up and teaching—my students were used to this, at least the ones that had been with me for a while. My dog, a black Labrador mix named Domino, was pretty good at helping me up. He just showed up at the barn one day and became mine. Domino was pretty chunky and stood still, letting me use his back or collar to help myself up when I fell. He stayed there until I was off the ground and wouldn't let horses near me during these instances. Domino was never trained for any of that. He just had good instincts and extreme loyalty. I rescued him, and now he rescued me time and again.

I also loved working at a daycare and interacting with the kids, but found myself taking more falls there as well. I just got so tired, and when I failed to slow down, I ended up losing my legs right out from under me. Many people do not know how to handle that, or it scares them when I fall. I just try to get up, brush myself off, and keep on going. I have never wanted people to take pity on me, but I needed someone there in case I required help.

***

Being a teacher and instructor has left a legacy of sorts. It's a great feeling to know that several of my students made it and went the extra mile to get to where they wanted to be. After I became an instructor, I wanted to be a vet or vet assistant and thought about going back to school. This was something I was passionate about. I always tried to learn everything I could from my vet, not just because of my own horses, but because everything about that field of veterinary medicine fascinated me. But honestly, being a vet assistant was too dangerous a career for someone with a disease like mine.

Call me crazy, but the smell of horses and fresh bailed hay and shavings really gave me a relaxing comfort that I needed before I went home. This was my time—my personal therapy—whether I rode or just groomed the horses. Grooming was relaxing for me and my favorite part of it all. I loved making my horses look nice, and I'm sure they felt better, especially after being hosed off on a hot day.

I look back on my glory years of showing, when I had to be on a horse almost all day. Now I count my blessings if I can stay on for an hour or so due to the bursitis in my hip, which flares up painfully. My legs are extremely weak when I'm done. There were times, though, that I just told myself I could push through the pain because it needed to be done.

Going through this, if I have a bad week pain-wise and can't get back on a horse until the following week, it's almost like starting all over again. The soreness comes back, and my legs don't want to work. The hip pain is no fun.

I'll mention here that my circulation was (and is) so bad, it's difficult to keep warm enough—a reoccurring theme throughout my life. Riding a horse never helped with my circulation, but it did keep me warm when I rode bareback. Oddly, I never used a heating blanket during my childhood in New Jersey, but began to lose some circulation in college. By the time I arrived in Texas, I seemed to need the extra warmth, especially when the winters rolled around. I keep a heating blanket on my bed and use one on my favorite chair when I watch TV. My legs and feet just don't warm up on their own. My neuropathy seems to be getting worse.

Realizing that my horseback riding days are coming to an end makes me feel, well, dismal. It has been such a big part of my life, and it will, in some way, still be part of it— just not always on the back of a horse. Teaching really helps. I still get to enjoy my horses and let another person understand the wonderful things these animals can offer.

And it's not just the horseback riding. It's the daily waking up and facing the day. There are instances when my body just says, No, you can't do that at all. I might have something planned, but my legs don't necessarily cooperate. Needless to say, it bothered me that there would be ever-increasing limitations on my life in a way I had not comprehended before.

I fought it. I really did. But it seemed no matter how much I tried; nothing increased my strength. I became depressed, and yes, it shook my faith. I felt like God had stricken me with this horrible disease, so I couldn't enjoy life like I really wanted to. It was very difficult to deal with.

CHAPTER 8
MARRIAGE AND MOTHERHOOD

Aerodynamically the bumblebee shouldn't be able to fly, but the bumblebee doesn't know that, so it goes on flying anyway.
~ Mary Kay Ash

I suffer from a physical disease that may "set me apart" from the general population in the view of some, but otherwise, I'm just like any other person. I experience problems in my life, just like anyone else. Everyone suffers from some sort of issue or stressor, and some are worse than others. When dealing with other problems on top of my disease, it tends to make my physical problems worse. I don't think people realize this fact. My tremors increase, which means the doctors want me to take more medications to control them. When I lose sleep due to worries about the issues in my life, I fall more frequently and am afraid of breaking bones.

I mentioned earlier that I met my first husband in East Texas. The year was 1993. Sometimes I wish I would have continued on to Corpus Christi because I think my life would have been much different. I wouldn't have gone through a horrible divorce with my first husband and been mentally and physically abused by him. But then again, without that marriage, I would not have had my wonderful son.

This is something I have in common with many, many women. Regardless of age, ethnicity, culture or disability, domestic abuse is a thread that runs through many families. I think as women, it binds us together, especially when we realize we are not alone in our circumstances and speak out against it. And I think the coping strategies mentioned in the previous chapters have a lot to do with how I survived it.

We married in 1994 and divorced in 2011, spending almost eighteen years together. It had started out happily enough. He was younger than me by about two years and a typical charmer. He took me out to dinners, movies, dancing and would say all of the right things.

Before Ryan was born, I suspected that my husband might be having an affair. The woman in question had a husband with whom I happened to be friends, and he also thought they were spending too much time in each other's company. We all rode horses together, but my husband and his wife hung out without us at the local cafe.

Then came the phone calls at night from a family member confirming that he was cheating on me. It was hard to believe him when he denied it. He also had started drinking more, which I didn't like. All he did was come home after stopping at the cafe and go to sleep. He was mostly on the night shift, so we had opposite schedules except for the weekend. We did separate once but worked things out.

Pregnancy and CMT

We lived in a brand new trailer in Douglass for a few years and started thinking about getting pregnant. We moved to Nacogdoches to be closer to the doctor's office. Then we got our first real house, and it didn't take us that long to get pregnant at all.

After going through genetic testing, I thought that I had a clear understanding of what would happen. We were told by the doctors that if we had a boy, there was less of a risk that he would contract the disease. If I had a girl, there was a 50/50 shot that she would have CMT, but the degree shouldn't be any worse than what I had.

I did not believe it was something they could predict with certainty; it was obviously just an educated guess. I had lost confidence in doctors in general, and these statistics didn't hold much weight with me. I knew that I was ready to start a family, but I was scared to death. I didn't want to subject another human being to what I had been through, even though there are a lot of worse things that could happen. After much discussion with my husband, we decided to take it in stride, and we would be grateful for whatever happened.

In November of 1997, I found out that I was pregnant! I wanted to try and do everything right for this baby so that, maybe, the risks would be lower. I just wanted to believe that anything would help. I started reading all of the books on babies and pregnancies that I could get my hands on. About three-to-four months into the pregnancy, I had an ultrasound, and it revealed that we would be having a baby boy. I was very relieved. There was less of a chance for a boy to develop CMT.

I was not warned about an important issue—the weight in the front of me made falling more likely. I took many falls once I had a belly. One time I even fell headfirst into the corner of my dad's desk. When these kinds of spills happened, I always called the doctor to make sure I had nothing to worry about. I'm sure the OB/GYN was getting tired of me, but I felt I could never be too cautious.

The morning Ryan was born, I got up and went to the bathroom. I noticed my underwear was wet. I admit to being a bit naive and not really understanding the significance of it. I did call the hospital and was told it was normal, since I wasn't having contractions. My best friend from New Jersey, Amy, was visiting, and so we went to the movies along with my husband. As I sat in the theater, I grew progressively wetter, not realizing it was amniotic fluid. I was in labor the whole time we were at the movies!

So, my water didn't break. It simply leaked, then seeped. We headed straight to the hospital after the movie was over, even though I was ready to go do something else, but Amy and my husband were convinced that I needed to be checked. Once the doctor took a look at me, he said it was definitely amniotic fluid, and he would have to break my water, then labor would begin. After four hours of being in labor and not dilating, the doctor didn't want my body to go through more stress. I had a C-section and delivered a healthy baby boy on July 19, 1998, about 10 p.m. at the Nacogdoches Medical Center. He was eight pounds and almost eleven ounces. Everything looked great, and all of the scores given to my baby were in the normal range. There was no test to tell if he would carry the gene for CMT until he was older, and for now, we couldn't have asked for a healthier baby.

I have to mention that I must have cloned myself, for Ryan looked so much like me. Same eyes, facial shape, mouth—a cutie patootie if I say so myself. I felt so blessed that I would enjoy the special bond between boys and their mothers that I had heard about: the snuggles, the hugs, and the heart-melting smiles.

Amy was there for all of it and couldn't believe her best friend—the little girl with braces and a mullet—was now a Mommy!

I spent the next two weeks helping Dawn the best I could. I remember being asleep in the guest bedroom one night, and at some point, Dawn basically barged into the room. She had Ryan in her arms and looked equal parts ready to cry and ready to scream. She asked me, but pretty much told me, "Can you please take him?" I dutifully got up, took the tiny, crying baby in my arms and went out to the big chair in the living room. I'll never forget looking at the beautiful little man and feeling love like I never had before. The next morning, they found me asleep in one of the oversized chairs with Ryan on my chest.

After my pregnancy, my body changed just as everyone's does, but what they didn't tell me was that a person with a neuromuscular disorder could have nerve damage from the weight that was gained from carrying the baby. From then on, I was on a downward spiral with my health. I lost a lot of function in my right hand, and my sciatica nerves act up often. It doesn't mean that all of it was related to the pregnancy, but it sure didn't help the disease.

All of this led to more medications to make me as comfortable as possible. I tried to only take it when absolutely needed, so I didn't begin to rely too heavily on the meds. I took medication that helped numb my shooting leg pain—sometimes it was so bad, I could hardly stand. I still take tremor medications I took back then. They are stronger and taken more frequently, with a different mixture to help me at different times of the day.

I didn't learn about any of these things until the pain started to become unmanageable. Post-pregnancy, my back and hip pain got so bad that I had to take a stronger medication than ibuprofen, which meant prescription anti-inflammatories. Again, they are still something I take today.

Life was always changing, but in my world, it seemed to change a lot more often and when I least expected it. I almost hated to look forward to anything because I never knew how my body is going to feel on any given day. Still, I wouldn't change a thing. Knowing that Ryan would almost certainly be my only child made him even more precious, and bringing him into the world was certainly worth anything I had to endure residually.

Life After Baby

We lived in our house for about five years and then started building our new home in Douglass, so Ryan would be in a good school district. I was stressed and tried to attend to my health through aqua therapy at a gym called NRG. Certain exercises in the pool were really beneficial. I went for a few months off and on when I could because insurance didn't cover all of it. I tried to do this when Ryan was in school and in between horse riding instruction. A few times, Ryan and his father came with me—Ryan was a handful to keep off the gym equipment.

I must say that I can swim and ride horses better than I can walk, and while swimming is a great form of exercise, riding horses is even better. Not only is it wonderful being with these magnificent creatures, but I use my muscles in a totally different way when riding. The doctors always wanted me to swim; they didn't believe the riding was as helpful. But I was the one living through the disease and can ensure anyone that horseback riding is amazingly beneficial.

In the meantime, my marriage had many ups and downs. After we had lived in our new home for about ten years, the trouble really started. He just pulled away and told me he was jealous about all the time I had to put into Ryan's care, starting from when Ryan was a baby and continuing into toddlerhood. In 2011, I faced the hardest decision I've ever had to make. My marriage was no longer what I thought it should be, and there were many disappointments, much more than the average marital spats. Plus, I wanted someone I could talk to—not someone who just wanted to sit and watch television and occasionally play with Ryan, but otherwise remain detached and uninvolved. I was very depressed, unhappy and wearing myself out with worry about what to do.

I felt that if I gave up, I'd be a failure to myself, as well as my family. I have felt failure many times before in dealing with my disease, but I never thought I would feel it with my family. I really didn't want to break my family up, but was at my wit's end. I did not want it to hurt my son, but he also was being affected by what was going on already. What should I do? What could I do?

I had tried everything I could think of—talking with my husband, going to counseling by myself (he wouldn't go), fervently praying, talking with my pastor and friends—you name it, I tried it. But nothing seemed to make anything better. I just wanted the love to return that had left the marriage so long ago. It was breaking me on the inside, yet I had to hold it together on the outside for my son.

Oh, I questioned my role in all of this. Was it the disease and dealing with all my issues that were tearing us apart? Well, it had never affected us before, or at least I assumed so. My husband didn't want to communicate, so I really didn't know the reasons. As I contemplated divorce, I knew Ryan would suffer and didn't want that for him. I wanted to be the family that stayed together for eternity. But I had to do something for me and my sanity rather than worry about everyone else's feelings at this point. That was a lot easier said than done. I was sick to my stomach with worry.

Thankfully, God answered my prayer about what to do regarding my marriage. He sent my husband away on a new job adventure on an onshore drilling rig. I wasn't really even consulted about the new job but thought it was for the best because my husband was gone anywhere from sixteen to twenty-one days at a time. This gave us time apart to see what our feelings really were.

I was doing all the household errands and transporting Ryan to his appointments, taekwondo, school drop-offs and pick-ups, and whatever else might come up. Adding all that on top of everything else was a challenge, but I was up for it. I figured it would give me a taste of single motherhood in the event I did get divorced.

On the bright side, I didn't have to cook as much and could cook healthier meals. On the downside, there was no health insurance for my son. That's always a problem with switching jobs— finding affordable insurance, especially in the case of having preexisting conditions. I found an insurance policy—it didn't offer the best coverage, but it was better than nothing.

Divorce

Of course, there were counseling sessions regarding my marriage and divorce. Through those sessions, I learned that other sources of counseling exist as well, such as visiting with our pastors, priests, rabbis, etc. I went to my pastor on several occasions, as well as a counselor. But Ryan's dad only went to one counseling session. He resisted the help. The thing about counseling is that people have to be willing to attend and want to solve issues. Otherwise, it's futile.

Ultimately, I did not see any other choice but to divorce, and my husband happened to agree. I really did not expect that. I thought maybe he might ask what he could do to make it better, but he didn't show much remorse or a care in the world. But when he returned from his shift, he seemed shocked to be served divorce papers. However, the situation was so bad that I was willing to face the future as a divorced single mother, wondering how I could support my son and myself while maintaining the standard of living we were used to. It seemed impossible, for I had to support us on the income that I was making at the time, and my husband would help only to the point he was required to—he made that clear. The court system made him pay enough so that we were able to survive.

Honestly, all I really needed him as the significant other in my life was to do what is expected of him. My marriage lasted as long as it did for Ryan's sake—the last five or so years were very unhappy. Ryan was thirteen when the divorce was finalized. He still needed a father, but I couldn't go on. I was basically a single mom anyway, with all of his travels. Even when he was home, he didn't participate.

I was very concerned about Ryan. They say divorce is the toughest on the children, and he had already endured so much. It truly broke my heart. On top of that, the increased stress exacerbated the problems I had with my disease. It magnified all the normal problems and made the physical problems worse. But the bottom line in all of this was that I managed and coped. I became an independent woman for my son, and we managed quite well.

Well, at least until the girlfriend bomb was dropped. Yes, my ex-husband got a girlfriend not long after our divorce, and Ryan seemed okay with her until she began monopolizing all of his dad's time. Ryan just wanted time alone with his dad, and that set off a whole new wave of problems. My son was just getting used to the divorce situation, and then had to deal with getting used to this woman and her three kids. To say the least, I was not a happy person because of the lack of respect for our son's feelings. Nothing like adding more stress to an already stressful situation!

The girlfriend went to wife status not too long afterward, and it was basically shoved in everyone's face. At least that is what it felt like. Eventually, Ryan did not like visiting with his dad anymore. He didn't like his stepmom or step-siblings. I can't say that I blame him, for he didn't have a bed or a room at his dad's house. He was told that if he wanted to stay over, he could sleep on the couch or the recliner.

Ryan told him, "No, Dad, I'm not going to stay until I have a room."

I was very proud of him for standing up for what he believed he deserved. He should have been given his own space, just like being in his own home. That marriage didn't last long, and the cycle started again. Finally, after two or three more girlfriends, Ryan said, "Dad, I don't want to meet your girlfriends unless you are really serious about them."

Cancer Scare

What else could be thrown at me to make life any harder? I don't think I really wanted to know the answer to that. But the next thing that came my way was the possibility of cancer. I always said that God had given me enough with the muscular dystrophy and that I hoped and prayed that I would never have to deal with cancer on top of it, but here it was.

In July, I was told that my body contained a virus that could cause cervical cancer. However, my body should be able to fight off the virus on its own, and it would likely never develop into cancer. My fear was that since I already had a form of muscular dystrophy, my immune system might not fight it off. People with muscular dystrophy and CMT tend to have weakened immune systems. It didn't seem to bother the doctors, though, so maybe I shouldn't be as concerned. It kept creeping up in the back of my mind.

The doctors just told me we had to keep an eye on it and had me come in every six months to make sure it did not turn into cancer. I was terrified, to say the least, and kept praying it would not lead to cancer. I had no one to turn to except my pastor and ex-husband, and I thought my ex had a right to know for Ryan's sake in case something did get worse. I was trying to keep it quiet, so my son would not find out and become afraid of losing his mother. The fewer people that knew about it, the better. It took a year, but my body fought it away. Praise God!

That wasn't my only battle with the big C, unfortunately. A few years later, I was at the doctor's office, and a nurse noticed an oversized mole on my back. The next thing I knew, I was having surgery to remove the mole and make sure it was not cancerous. It was another scary waiting game, but once again, it came back non-cancerous! I hope and pray that I never have to hear that something on my body may be cancerous again.

Ryan always loved his baths!

One of my favorite nicknames for Ryan was "Cutie Patootie."

One of Amy's visits to Texas to see us. We both loved to visit with her.

Ryan loved dressing up as Batman and still had that blanket as an adult. He would sometimes sleep with it under his pillow.

CHAPTER 9
MY SON AND HIS DISABILITY

Start by doing what's necessary; then do what's possible; and suddenly you are doing the impossible.
~ Francis of Assisi

In the same timeframe as the divorce, I had taken Ryan to get a blood test to see if he had CMT. He had been exhibiting some symptoms, and I was concerned. There are so many different forms of the disease, and the only way to tell if he was being affected was to do a blood test, which was fairly simple considering what I went through for a diagnostic screening.

It was very strange, as well as scary, sitting there with my son and waiting to know what the results might be. I remembered how scared I was at his age and watched how nervous he was. I couldn't help but try to make him laugh and take his mind off of it by tickling him and just being silly. But ultimately, it was in God's hands, and only He knew what we were going to face.

I sat there and prayed silently for my son that he would not be stricken with what I had, and also for his comfort and understanding that things would be okay even if he had CMT. We could handle things together, and I would be able to help him through everything since I had already been in his position. I will say, it wasn't anything I thought I would have to do, but it was time to face reality.

I had always known that there was a possibility of him having the same disease, and while I was as comforting and confident on the outside as possible, on the inside, I didn't want Ryan to struggle through life like I had, never knowing what problem may be around the next corner. How would he deal with all of the names he might be called by other kids and learn to get back up when he fell or stumbled or tripped? There would be challenges that he'd never yet imagined.

Great Trip for Distraction

From Amy's perspective:

In 2008 I moved from NJ to Green Bay, Wisconsin. I had just ended a long-term relationship, and the town I was living in was getting way too crowded for me. I wanted a fresh start somewhere new, but I wanted to know somebody familiar with the area. My brother had moved to Green Bay with his wife at the time. The relationship ended, but he decided to stay in the area. This was during the Great Recession, so it took longer than expected for me to find gainful employment. It did not take long to find a boyfriend – and just for the record, I wasn't looking! I met Andrew in June of 2008, and we got engaged in October of 2009. We decided on a June 2011 wedding date. I would be just shy of 40 years old by then, so we chose to have a casual wedding in our back yard. I, of course, asked Dawn and Ryan if they would like to be part of our wedding party, and they both said yes. Once again, Dawn was concerned about walking on the uneven ground of our back yard and just like at her own wedding, she put her mind to it and made it happen. She would walk with Ryan holding onto his arm and using a cane that she beautifully decorated! At 13 years old, Ryan was the youngest of the groomsmen. I have a treasured photo of him and me before the ceremony; we are both grinning like crazy, and his braces are on full display. The next day a group of us walked down the road to visit Bay Beach Amusement Park. It is an incredible small amusement park nestled on the east side of Green Bay.

Ryan and Amy before her wedding

Left to right: My mom, me, Amy and Ryan after the ceremony

The Diagnosis

Well, Ryan was diagnosed with CMT1A, just like me. The immediate challenge was getting him through taekwondo classes. He wanted to be a black belt and do leadership training. He was never restricted on what he did in class, but eventually, there were kicks that took some extra work to learn. He had great power but just needed a lot of extra work on balance. The further he went, the more balance he needed.

My job was to show him how to stand strong, no matter what challenge he came across and to rely solely on his faith in God. He needed a lot of encouragement, and as his mother, I was prepared to help him in any way possible. I had made it this far with no one in my family knowing what to expect from the disease, so I knew we had a head start since I have been living with it.

Fortunately, my son and I were able to meet these challenges. Ryan was strong enough to help me out when I needed it, especially at the barn. We fed in the evenings on the weekends, and this kept him strong. He would need that strength for what was to come.

He dealt with it all amazingly. Perseverance became a critical part of his values. As I watched him grow through the years, he showed great character in dealing with his CMT up to the day of his death at the age of twenty.

I had my share of surgeries by the time I was forty and knew how to comfort Ryan through his first procedure at Shriners Hospital, for he was extremely nervous at having his Achilles tendon lengthened by making some incisions in his calf. Then they moved a tendon from the outside part of his foot towards the top of his foot to help straighten out his ankle. This would help him tolerate braces better and possibly correct him to the point of not needing braces later on.

They operated on his left foot first, and if it showed great improvement, he would have the right one done. The left ankle was the most worrisome of his conditions, bending out so bad that he had a huge callous on the outside of his foot. Sometimes it hurt him so badly that he didn't want to walk.

Ryan was terrified of being put under anesthetic regardless of how many people told him it would be okay and that he'd wake up from it. He also didn't know what to expect after surgery. We were told he would be laid up for six weeks but would be able to return to school after a week on crutches or in a wheelchair. This depended on whether they put in the steel plate above his big toe to prevent a floppy toe from happening.

All of the surgeries were done through Shriners Hospital in Houston, and they did an excellent job with him. He became comfortable because they explained everything step-by-step. Once he understood the procedure, we scheduled it for a few weeks later. Up until the day of his surgery, I can't tell you how many questions I answered regarding it. He was still nervous but ready to get it over with. Thankfully, he came through with flying colors and didn't need the steel plate after all. The procedure took longer than expected anyway, but once he was awake enough, we were able to go home and start the recovery process.

His dad was at the hospital from morning until night. As we talked about going home, Ryan asked if his Dad would spend the night to help him go to the bathroom. His dad consulted with his new wife; he agreed to stay over if she could stay over as well. I was not cool with this at all. His father and stepmother followed us all the way home. Little did we know that the anesthesia was going to make Ryan sick, and we made several stops to accommodate his vomiting. It made for a very long car ride—two and a half hours with a very nauseated boy.

When we arrived home, my mother and I got Ryan settled into the house. His father and stepmother showed up; his father came in while his stepmother sat in the car. Ryan reiterated that he wanted his dad to sleep on the floor next to him, but without his stepmother. His father's reaction was to go out to the driveway and sit in the car. They planned to sleep in the car, and I told them to leave. They gave me a hard time for a while about wanting to stay, but I locked everything up, and they finally left after midnight.

The first few days were challenging for me because I couldn't get his bleeding to stop. I set up a baby monitor so I could hear him in his room. Ryan stayed in his bed and walked as little as possible. I changed the gauze frequently, but it didn't stop bleeding until after the third or fourth day. I didn't have any help with taking care of him either and was tiring quickly.

Ryan was uncomfortable with the pain after surgery and was prescribed pain pills.

Normally, I wouldn't like giving pain medicine like this to my child, but it helped him get much-needed rest. He used a wheelchair at home and school until he was comfortable with crutches. His teachers and friends were very helpful in getting him out of the car and into the building. Even during the day, his friends helped him around and even decorated his wheelchair, but there were still the few ignorant kids who just wouldn't lift a finger to help.

When I took Ryan back to Shriners to have his checkup, they removed the cast, and the doctor liked how it healed. Now it was time to have him fitted with the new braces—AFOs. It was amazing. We were never charged anything. The second surgery was just a few months away, but this time he wasn't so nervous. He wasn't thrilled, of course, to go through it again, but at least he knew what to expect. I was more prepared at home for unexpected problems and stocked up on gauze. This time around, everything went more smoothly. They even gave him anti-nausea medicine before the ride home.

Pet Peeves

I will be honest—I list a host of pet peeves throughout this book. But some amusement parks rank pretty high on the list. As Ryan and I waited during those appointments, we talked about the amusement parks he enjoyed. He loved any kind of theme park and was a roller coaster fanatic.

He loved Sea World in San Antonio, Six Flags in Dallas and San Antonio, and Disney World in Florida. It brought back some not-so-pleasant memories of getting nasty stares due to walking up the exit ramps at Six Flags, and so we talked about this particular pet peeve.

The only reason that we went up the exit ramps was because Six Flags has no other way for people in wheelchairs to access the rides. Six Flag actually issued wristbands to allow us to do so. Now there is a whole new system in place for wheelchair-bound Six Flags tourists. Instead of a wristband allowing us to enter the ride from the exit ramp, we now get a booklet, and the ride attendant tells us a time to come back and ride. This is because "normal people" complained about the unfairness of the exit ramp access for people with disabilities.

Really! Now we had to make our way up the exit ramps twice because of stupid people like this. I figured they were just jealous that we didn't have to wait in line. What they don't realize is that it's not easy going against traffic on exit ramps full of crazed park riders of all ages. People around us are in a rush and don't think about those who might need a bit more time and space to move or need accessibility due to a disability.

True, most have never heard of CMT. It's so rare that it made Ryan and I feel invisible at times. Even when people are in a wheelchair, others don't always stop. Yes, people in wheelchairs get bumped and jostled at times. However, the opposite is true for the person in the wheelchair—he or she has no choice but to stop for massive crowds of people who come off the rides. Again, it's that feeling of invisibility that aggravates us so.

I would have loved to be able to wait in line like everyone else, but couldn't. Ryan could have, but his feet tired quickly. I even tried bringing all of this up to a couple of the parks that we visited later, and all they had to say is, "We're sorry, but that is just our rules. Many people have complained that the people in wheelchairs were getting on quicker than they were." I really couldn't believe what I was hearing. I think all of us "wheelchair people" who enjoy the parks need to get together and form a meeting or rally to prove our point. It would make life much easier if people were more understanding and educated.

Don't get me wrong; there are some nice people out there who will actually step to the side and let us pass or hold the gate so we can get in, but for the most part, they are just plain rude. I decided to continue to take my son because he enjoyed it, and I liked riding some of the rides too, but the parks have really ruined it for the disabled people who really don't have any other choice but to follow the arbitrary rules.

CHAPTER 10
A SURGERY OF MY OWN

A hero is an ordinary individual who finds the strength to persevere and endure in spite of overwhelming obstacles.
~ Christopher Reeve

After Ryan had his surgeries, I wondered if the same type of surgery would benefit me. We both had the same problems with our feet, so I talked to his doctors at Shriners. They told me that surgery very well could help, but I would have to see a doctor outside of Shriners since they only treat kids eighteen years and younger.

Once I had Ryan all healed up and doing well, I started calling around to see if there were doctors that would lengthen my Achilles tendon. I talked with a few different offices and met with a surgeon a few weeks later. He went over my health history and what he thought about performing this procedure on me. He thought it would be a good procedure, although I was apprehensive because it was major surgery, and he would operate on both legs at once. That meant six weeks of no driving or doing much of anything.

I needed to arrange for someone to help with Ryan and get him back and forth to school. He was old enough now to help with many things around the house if I needed him, but he wasn't driving yet. Fortunately, my friend, who lived around the corner, said she could transport him and help me if needed. Her kids went to the same school. Since that part was figured out, I went ahead and scheduled my surgery.

On the day of my surgery, my parents drove me. I was already nervous enough, and my dad's driving didn't help my nerves. He was a very fast driver and changed lanes quickly and haphazardly, so it made for a scary ride. I was thankful that we arrived in one piece and was ready for a sedative, that's for sure!

I remember being prepped for the surgery and talking with the doctor about the procedure. The next thing I knew, it was all over with, and I was in recovery. I was told that the procedure went well, and I needed to go home and rest. They gave me a number to call in case I had any problems or questions. Making the ride home was another adventure since I had to ride with my legs propped up—and my dad, the crazy driver, was at the wheel. I did have a hard time staying on the seat during the ride home. I was ready to throw up in the backseat. I certainly didn't want food, but all he wanted to talk about was food.

Thankfully, I arrived back home in one piece. I was supposed to keep my legs elevated as much as possible and not walk very much for the first fourteen days. This was supposed to keep the swelling down and promote healing. Trying to maneuver around with two heavy, awkward casts was very difficult. I already had problems moving around without casts, so now the extra five pounds of weight on each leg made it challenging to lift my legs. I was given walking shoes, so I wasn't walking directly on the casts, but it didn't mean that it wasn't painful.

My sister was in town and stayed with me when she could. One night she attempted to make me dinner. All I remember was the corn on the cob and a messy kitchen. So I did get up to clean on that occasion but just appreciated that she cooked for me at all.

***

Around the fifth week, I started experiencing a lot of pain near where I assumed the incision was located. Since the casts covered my whole leg below my knee, I didn't know where the incision was, exactly. I wasn't having any problems before this, so I was unsure of what it could be. I put a call in with the nurses to see what the doctor had to say. When they got back to me, they just told me that I would have it looked at in a week and a half.

In the meantime, the pain seemed to get worse each day. I called again, and I was told just to hang in there, and they would look at it when I came in. Finally, I had them move my appointment to an earlier time slot so I could get the casts off and figure out what was going on to cause me so much pain. When I went in for my appointment, the doctor's comment was, "Well, you sure have been unhappy this past week."

Really, you think so? I thought. Why are some doctors like that, so void of empathy and a bedside manner? I will never understand it.

Anyway, he finally took the casts off and didn't see any reason why I should be having pain. He asked me to get up and walk. When I tried, my legs were so weak that I couldn't. So, the doctor looked at me with confusion. He couldn't understand why I was having such a hard time. I remember him saying very sarcastically, "Am I going to have to get a wheelchair in here so you can be wheeled out?" He acted like I should not have a problem walking since the casts were off. He offered to write me a prescription for physical therapy, and that was it. He left the room, and they got a wheelchair to take me to the front of the hospital. That doctor made me so angry. He just wrote me off like my concerns weren't important.

I did get back into working out slowly, as well as going to PT to try and get some strength back, but nothing seemed to help. I was stronger than I was when the casts came off, but not the same as I was before surgery. No one was able to figure out why until I went back to my orthotics specialist, and she figured that the surgery shouldn't have been done. The tightness in my Achilles is what helped me balance, and now I had to balance over a weakened ankle. In other words, I should never have had a surgery that was going to weaken that part of my body. That was why balancing was so much harder—the surgery harmed me rather than helped.

Doctors should know this kind of information. We trust them with our wellbeing, and in my case, a major part of my wellbeing was destroyed. I regretted having that surgery and still do since my ability to walk was further affected. In hindsight, I wonder why I didn't sue. I suppose it's because I have always focused on overcoming obstacles, and this was just another unfortunate circumstance to overcome. In hindsight, perhaps I should have availed myself of every legal recourse available simply to ensure this particular surgeon harmed no one else. To this day, I doubt he realizes how terribly the surgery has impacted my mobility for the worse.

I mentioned that as a child, I learned not to put a lot of trust in doctors, and this surgery confirmed those feelings. My podiatrist actually told me that I probably knew more about my disease than he did. I was kind of glad to hear a doctor admit that, but at the same time, it disturbed me. More than likely, other doctors feel the same way but don't want to admit it. Frankly, patients shouldn't know more about the disease than the doctors. But living with CMT, a rare disease, seems to be the exception. My journey is filled with first-hand experiences that few understand, but doctors should be more knowledgeable, so they can provide us with better care.

That is probably why people stop me when I'm in town shopping. They see my glaring symptoms and my gait and maneuverability issues, and it appears similar to theirs or someone they know. They are thirsting for more information about it. Indeed, I found the lack of knowledge in the medical community impacts many people who suffered from CMT or something very similar.

Their choice of doctor even makes a difference regarding what the disease might be called. Over the years, I have heard several different names for

CMT—Rousey Leavy, Spasmodic Torticollis, and CMT with tremors because some don't believe it includes tremors. It's no wonder that people receive confusing and mixed messages when medical professionals are confused themselves.

***

Once Ryan's surgeries were behind him, not to mention mine, it was time to move on.

I wanted to make sure that the rest of Ryan's time in high school went smoothly. He did well but started battling tremors in his hands and neck. I know it bothered him that getting food into his mouth became more difficult. Kids asked him what was wrong, and he just told them it was a part of his problem. I knew that crushed him inside, but he was trying to be tough on the outside.

Sounds familiar, right? I think Ryan learned from me how to play it cool, even when he was embarrassed. As a mother, it hurt my heart, especially when there wasn't much I could do except set the example. I was used to getting the strangest looks, but he was still learning to desensitize himself to it. Once again, it all had to do with a lack of knowledge and awareness in our cultures. Schools and households should share information about how to interact with people who have disabilities.

Once Ryan was a sophomore, I finally got a meeting with the school to set up a 504 plan—formal help for K-12 students who are struggling with a disability. His 504 status went out to his teachers, making them aware of his CMT diagnosis and requiring that he receive the help he needed. For example, the teachers knew to place him in the front of his class, so he didn't have to climb over backpacks in the middle of the aisle. This helped prevent him from falling. The 504 plan followed him the rest of his school career even through college, and it was a relief to know he would receive the help required so that he could master topics to the best of his abilities.

Ryan was accepted into Texas State Technical College to explore his love for the technical computer world. Yes, my son became a techie. His teachers knew he could not type fast and accommodated his disability. It was a very exciting time for him, and I was the proudest mom on planet earth, knowing Ryan had mastered a trade that was needed worldwide and sparked his entrepreneurial spirit. That young man was a whiz with computers.

Ryan on his last senior field trip

Senior celebration at First Baptist Church

Ryan being silly before his last high school dance

CHAPTER 11
THE PAIN JOURNEY

Your success and happiness lies in you. Resolve to keep happy, and your joy and you shall form an invincible host against difficulties.
~ Helen Keller

I think the topic of pain merits an entire chapter—not just physical pain, but the emotional aspects. As I looked back on the years 2011- 2012, it was really challenging. Family issues, marital issues, divorce, the economic downturn—how much more was I going to have to go through? Wasn't splitting my family up enough? On a positive note, I discovered that it wasn't too bad being single. I enjoyed my time with Ryan and doing our "own thing" without a grumpy person around. On a negative note, the physical pain escalated along with the emotional pain.

I had to spend less time on my feet than I wanted, which was depressing. Pain, honestly, exacerbates whatever depression I might experience as I witness how CMT has gradually taken over my body. I promised myself to never let that happen and continued to fight it, despite the almost constant hip pain. It was excruciating and still is. My left leg pain located in the back of my leg and behind my knee is also excruciating. It radiates down to my ankle. Some nights I put the heating pad on, and it does help.

When I walk more than usual, I hurt more. Lately, I've experienced a lot of leg pain, from my thighs to my knee, usually alternating from one to the other. It's as if someone is squeezing my kneecap or sticking a needle in one spot, and I notice it more when it rains.

Speaking of pain, I experienced a level of emotional pain, as well. I remarried and moved into a trailer house with my second husband after Ryan had graduated from high school and was getting ready for college. My parents did not come to my wedding, which was hurtful at the time. I didn't understand why they refused to come but assumed they were probably upset that we were moving to Tyler. They might also have sensed I made a bad choice in a marriage partner and simply did not approve. However, that wasn't their decision to make, although admittedly, it turned out that they were right. It was a mistake.

We lived on my new husband's park property filled with 1970s-era trailers that he ran with his mom and sister. The plan was for me to help improve the park aesthetics and contribute toward the marketing. Unfortunately, my suggestions were not implemented. He and I really had a failure to communicate, or more precisely, he asked my opinions and never used them. Therefore, he wasn't making enough money, especially because he had given up his successful cleaning business in favor of running the park.

I felt trapped in a three-bedroom trailer with a total of three children, two adults and two dogs, which made it difficult to move around without tripping. I hoped my house would sell so we could get a better home. I could not stand living in a place so dirty and filthy. Mice infested the walls, and roaches invaded the kitchen—not for lack of me trying to keep it clean. Unfortunately, my house lingered on the market, so I had to find a job. I ended up working at Academy Sports + Outdoors as a receptionist and dressing room attendant.

This brought on more problems for me physically. When they hired me, I was not informed of all the job duties and ended up with "golfers elbow." Unlike tennis elbow that hurts on the outside of the elbow, my pain radiated on the inside of my arm to my elbow and was exacerbated by hanging up so many clothes with squeeze clamps. It felt like a pin was being pushed into my arm.

What husband would want his wife to endure more pain, but my husband just told me to keep on keeping on and assured me everything would be okay. It didn't help that I had a medical condition, and he had an aversion to hospitals. We had been through a lot with his sister slowly dying of cancer, so he was understandably tired of hospitals. I had to go in for some back injections, which probably didn't help his fear of the hospitals, but my hospital visits were only in and out.

I did need to go to the doctors often, and he didn't always go with me. But I know he didn't believe in doctors much because of his sister's situation, and he didn't have insurance coverage when he was sick.

By the time December 2016 came around, I couldn't take the living situation anymore or his kids' uncorrected attitude towards me (one of the hardest things to be is a stepparent). I thought we both agreed that it would be best if I moved back home until we could get a better living situation. It turns out, I think he was just tired of everything and saw me more as a problem or something that stood in his way. He also didn't like that I was miserable and wanted to move off of park grounds to have a more private life.

He filed for divorce after I moved out and brought the papers to me in January to start the process, and the day before Valentine's Day brought me the final divorce papers for my signature. Nice, couldn't he have waited a few days?

***

Back to physical pain. Through the years, I have always kept Tylenol and Ibuprofen handy to help with my falls and pain in general. Pain is just part of the disease, I guess. Relaxation was the only way to go, especially when it exceeds a "7" on the pain level scale. I default to a wheelchair when necessary because I want to remain mobile. However, wheelchair use can only go so far, as accommodations are usually an issue.

I've had so many falls in the past year that the chiropractor adjustments and massages were not helping all of the time. I went to my family doctor with this complaint, and he was able to put a cortisone injection in my hip and towards my back, which really helped the bursitis flair-ups. I just have to be careful not to start up too many activities before giving those areas enough rest, usually five to seven days.

Blood tests are always done to make sure that the levels in my blood stay in a healthy range for my liver and kidneys as well as other major body organs. It's important to make sure that the cortisone and anti-inflammatory medicine does not affect my major organs. My primary doctor and nurses are always vigilant about that. My doctor knows I have things I want to accomplish, and he's always given me positive reinforcement about getting the injections, but with a sprinkling of caution. People need to be careful of the doctors who are more than happy to give injections without asking too many questions.

There came a point in time in the years 2017 to 2018 when I went to a spine and joint specialist because the back pain went off the charts. It had become unbearable, and I'll bet many others with CMT understand exactly what I'm describing. The specialist did many test injections over the course of about six months. I was able to get the much stronger injections—some probably think of them as nerve blocks, but they are technically a neurotomy—that gave me relief over a much longer time period, sometimes lasting more than a year.

Lately, though, my back has given me problems. Thinking about the concept of pain takes me all the way back to middle school and the beginning of high school. I've been going to a chiropractor since before I could drive, around sixteen or seventeen years old. That's a long time to have back pain. I think it was then that I developed the "theme" of trying to push past all of the pain.

Not too long ago, I got my first test injection on my right side to see if the nerve blocks will be helpful again. The chiropractor can only do so much, but these nerve blocks are very helpful in stopping the pain for prolonged periods of time, thank God! When my pain exceeds my tolerance (and I have a high pain threshold), the shots make all the difference. Within two or three days, the pain becomes more bearable, and within a week, it's almost nonexistent. The injections generally last about a year, depending on how active I am. Over time, however, I've begun to build up some resistance to the shots. They don't seem to last as long or help the pain that much.

As I've grown older, my body continues to weaken. Falls, of course, happen more frequently if I push myself too much. This became quite evident just before Christmas of 2018. I took a tumble and got quite a shiner. *Oh great! Now I'll have a black eye for the holidays*, I thought. *Ho, ho, ho!*

As careful as I try to be, sometimes I fall several times a day.

One weekend I fell five times. My mind says to slow down, but my body isn't sure how to comply. The key, I've learned, is to take the slips and spills in stride. They are part and parcel of my life, and I take responsibility for managing these inevitable occurrences, both physically and emotionally. My family is aware of the toll it takes and tries to help me through it. I can't stress enough the importance of having a support system to help keep your attitude in check and your sense of humor running at full speed.

***

Fast forward to 2019. I do have constant pain at this stage of my life. I'm not going to lie—the older I get, the harder it is to get past all the pain on some days. I just want to stay curled up under my electric blanket, and rising above it is part of the daily routine.

People should understand how hard it is some days to put one foot in front of the other. It's not as easy as it looks. I just put on a smile as best I can and keep going, inspired by others who navigate a similar or more difficult path. Some suffer pain from simply writing their names. I don't necessarily have pain writing my name, but some thin pens are hard to hold.

I would call it a challenge, but at least I can dress myself when others cannot. However, with these new braces, it takes me an extra ten minutes to get ready. I have to use longer socks, place the brace correctly, slip my pants leg on, put my shoe on, and move on to my other leg with sock, brace, pant leg, and shoe.

Prescription bottles are sometimes bombproof for me. No matter how hard I try, I can't push and turn at the right time. Even over-the-counter meds are a challenge to open. What else is there for me to do but figure out a way around it? So teeth have become an invaluable source of opening things like medicine bottles. I'm sure that my parents would not appreciate that after spending so much on braces when I was younger. But I have to do what I can to make things work when other parts of my body don't want to.

Walking while wearing glasses was difficult because it affected my balance. I tried contact lenses. Putting them in wasn't such a problem... the problem was getting them out! My pincer grip, the grip of my thumb and pointer finger, was too weak to grab the contacts. I even taught my son how to grab them since he wanted to get rid of his glasses and opt for contacts. His grip was not yet affected, and I hoped it would remain that way. On top of that, I kept getting eye infections. Eventually, I had Lasik surgery to correct my vision once and for all.

Once again, this is just an example of how I adjusted my life according to what I can and cannot do and taught Ryan the same life skills. If there is something that I hope you take away from this, it is to never give up no matter the challenge. "Where there is a will, there is a way." The grace of God has guided me to figure things out or put someone in my life who is willing to help me. For that, I am very, very grateful.

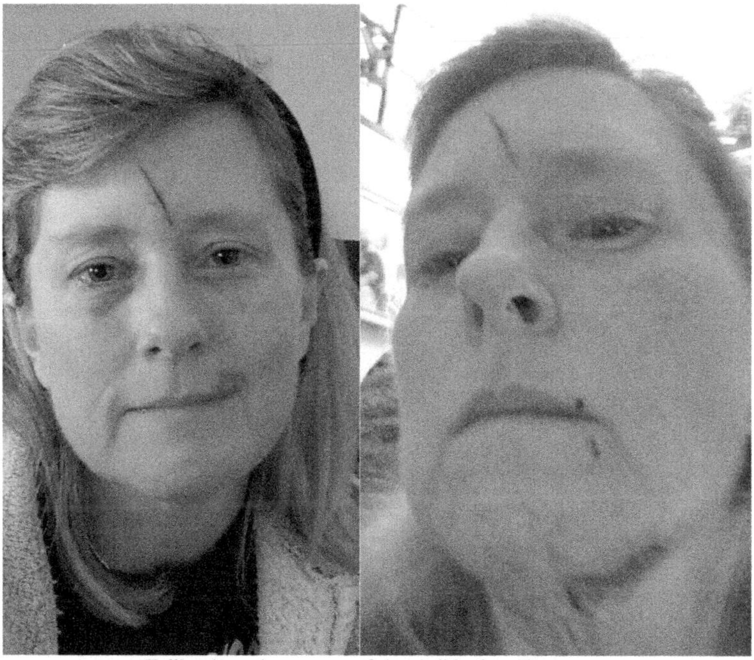

Falling into the corner of the wall before Christmas

CHAPTER 12
DEEP BRAIN STIMULATION

Abled does not mean enabled.
Disabled does not mean less abled.
~ Khang Kijarro Nguyen

I had a very hard time with my tremors leading up to my wedding with Frank in May 2019. I experienced dizziness from a mixture of medications that are supposed to control the tremors and pain. So, I had to consider a course of action.

I considered deep brain stimulation (DBS), which is a surgical procedure. Those who undergo DBS have an electrode implanted deep within their brains. The electrode delivers an amount of stimulation controlled by a device (like a pacemaker). A wire connects the electrode to the device, which is placed in the chest under the skin.

As I read more about DBS, however, the more I wondered about all the risks. I do want the tremors to stop or ease up, but there are some serious side effects, according to the American Association of Neurological Surgeons. This includes stroke, temporary tingling in the face or limbs, temporary pain/swelling at the implantation site, allergic reaction to the implant, slight paralysis, speech or vision problems, jolting or shocking sensation, loss of balance, dizziness, reduced coordination, concentration difficulties.

Frankly, I don't need any more dizziness or lack of coordination; thank you very much.

So honestly, I was interested in DBS to help with my tremors but was terrified that the cure would be worse than the symptoms. I asked myself if I should just deal with the tremors and fight off the dizziness myself. I read that I should get DBS only if "my quality of life is compromised enough to be very unmanageable."

Was my life very unmanageable? Well, yes and no. I manage my life pretty well but have to drink coffee (and just about any other type of drink) through a straw. Sometimes a drink doesn't have to be full for me to spill it, and I have to keep covers on the glasses. Some days it feels like I am shaking from the inside all the way to the outside of my body. I just don't know how much longer I can deal with it, and to me, it feels like I am just "getting by."

Another factor had to be considered. At my DBS appointment, the word "neuropathy" was brought up for the first time that I can remember. None of my other physicians had discussed it with me. Actually, Frank is the one who first had suspicions and connected the dots while we were dating.

"You probably have neuropathy," I remember him commenting.

"Why would you say that?" I asked.

"Because you have tingling, and that's a symptom," he answered.

Frank explained that as a diabetic, he experienced the firsthand effects of tingling—especially in his feet. My own tingling manifests differently, as do other symptoms. For instance, I sometimes think my feet are cold, but they are actually warm when I touch them. Regardless, I was able to share Frank's hypothesis at my DBS appointment, and it turned out he was right.

My fingers are curled up due to neuropathy. I always assumed the coldness in my legs was due to a lack of circulation, but it has something to do with neuropathy, as well. After all, neuropathy is a neurological problem related to the nerves (neuro) and pathy (disease). But people can have neuropathy in their hands as well. Doctors at one point said I had muscle wasting in my wrist, which is attributed to CMT but is not part of the neuropathy.

DBS can help with neuropathy, but not my specific type of neuropathy. Patients who experience neuropathy with tremors haven't had much success with DBS —and I have both. Previously, I was getting Botox injections to control the tremors from a doctor in Tyler, who did a really good job. Suddenly, I was informed I would have to see someone else.

"Why?" I asked the nurse

"Because you are asking for too much medication and botox," was the answer.

Seriously? I was completely caught off guard with that explanation. I had never over-refilled these medications, nor would I ever consider doing so. I've always hated being on all the meds I have to take. The only thing I could conclude was that my ex-husband might have asked for refills when I was out of the room. When I went to the restroom, my ex-husband could have asked for some kind of medication. It's the only explanation I can think of. However, after talking to some other people, they said the doctor probably didn't want to treat me anymore because he had too many medicare patients and wanted to devote more time to surgeries. That is where he makes more money.

I wanted to keep getting the Botox injections—they do control my tremors for a couple of months at a time. But there is no one in my area I can trust. Previously, one doctor caused me to lose the function of my left arm. He thought he needed to go lower with the injection, although I questioned him about it. The result was devastating. I couldn't lift my left arm past shoulder height for a few weeks. Needless to say, I won't go back to him.

Even if I use my neurologist in my town, I'd have to buy the Botox at the pharmacy at nearly an expense of $500 out of pocket because my insurance provider considers it cosmetic. After purchasing it and bringing it to a doctor, I'd then have to pay the doctor to inject me.

He doesn't keep any in his office because he has had problems getting reimbursed from insurance. It is really a sad situation because it could be such an easy fix for my tremors, but the insurance companies ruin that.

***

Back to DBS. Long story short, my neurologist could not do much more for me, and that's why he referred me for a potential DBS surgery. I really wanted to talk to someone who had the procedure done for tremors like mine first but could find no one with my particular symptoms. Most patients have Parkinson, epilepsy or dystonia, which is quite different than CMT.

After weighing my options, I decided to take the plunge and have a DBS consultation. This required driving all the way to Houston and booking a hotel room for an overnight stay—quite an ordeal considering the drive time, traffic, and expense. My hope was that the trip would be worth it.

They did physical testing and a full work-up, first with the doctor's assistant who knew just as much about it as the doctor did.

"Do you want to be videotaped?" the assistant asked.

"Sure," I answered, knowing it would help them determine if I qualify for surgery.

When I was done, the actual doctor came in, and I did the same exact things for her. Based on the tests, she decided we should just do Botox injections in my neck rather than the DBS surgery. They didn't necessarily rule out DBS, but again, it hasn't yielded great results for people with tremors and CMT. I was both relieved and disappointed. On the one hand, I was thrilled that they wanted to try something nonsurgical. I wasn't looking forward to brain surgery and having a little metal device implanted in my chest.

However, in another sense, it was a letdown. I couldn't help but think, *Great, I came all this way and booked a hotel room, just to be told I need Botox.* The trip there was just so inconvenient, and I hated that I'd have to go all the way back to Houston for the Botox treatments. But at least I wouldn't have to purchase the Botox myself, for the neurological disorder clinic had it in stock. The same out-of-pocket doctor cost remained, however. I did arrange a follow-up Botox appointment and decided to look at the bright side. As I've mentioned before, Botox has helped me immensely in the past.

When I returned home and processed all that had occurred, I became emotionally uncomfortable. Actually, I felt a bit traumatized after replaying the testing in my mind over and over again. I thought I was doing pretty well until I witnessed myself undergoing those tests. Seeing myself struggle to perform was a reality check. It made me realize how disheartening my situation was, and I broke down and wept. I was not as strong as I thought I was, and it caused a lot of tears.

Frank, who was with me throughout this appointment, also thought I was doing well. I suppose he had become accustomed to my gait and the limitations I have with mobility, so my emotional reaction concerned him. He simply did what he does best, and that was to reassure me that he loved me just the way I am. This is the exact type of emotional support I hope and pray everyone has in their journey through CMT. In theory, I might have many future trips to the movement disorder clinic ahead of me. However, right now, I'm still paying for the last botox injection. Once again, the system is flawed because I wasn't told that the hospital was out of network with my insurance or that I was going to owe that much when I made the appointment at the movement disorder clinic.

I may not go back to Houston due to the time required for me to be off work, the expense of meals, and the fact I don't have enough insurance coverage. I got an extra bill from the neurological center due to my insurance. I'm hopeful that I can be seen at an MDA clinic in Houston that has a CMT specialist and a neurological clinic. The MDA clinic is awaiting my doctor's notes. Once they see my records, they can tell me their pricing. With any luck, they will be more affordable than the movement disorder clinic.

Only time will tell if DBS surgery becomes the best solution for me. It's as though people with disabilities are a science experiment—not that I'm complaining. At least there are new treatments being made available as the medical community searches for ways to address our symptoms.

A New Treatment for Tremors

Speaking of the brain, I've recently heard of the Neuravive Treatment for Essential Tremor, an incisionless outpatient treatment for essential tremor patients like me who have not responded to medication. It sounds interesting—check out https://usa.essentialtremor.com to learn more about this technology.

I am definitely curious about this type of ultrasound treatment, which uses sound energy deep in the brain, guided by MR imaging, that passes through the skull without the need for incisions, permanent implants or inserted probes. From what I understand, there is no exposure to radiation, and only a small area of tissue is targeted with heat to destroy a small spot on the brain (Vim nucleus of the thalamus) for a therapeutic effect.

Although this procedure isn't specifically for CMT patients, it seems to address the tremors that affect many of us. According to the website, results are immediate with minimal complications. It gives me hope that these types of new treatments will become widely available.

Again, the ongoing medical research to address the various symptoms we experience due to our disease is nothing short of incredible. We can all use the internet as a tool to find out more about deep brain stimulation, the Neuravive Treatment for Essential Tremor and other experimental treatments in the months and years ahead.

Insurance Reform

Speaking of our flawed insurance system, I have to say that writing a book is hard work, but it also gives the author a platform to discuss matters of importance. For me, insurance reform is long overdue. I noticed the slip in coverage when the doctor I had trusted ever since I got pregnant with Ryan went out of network. It has been downhill ever since.

We all deserve a doctor who fits our needs—one who is invested in our health, listens, actually reads our charts, and doesn't pass us off to nurses and physician assistants. Doctors today are stressed—there is too much paperwork required, especially for Medicare, and therefore doctors are avoiding Medicare patients. Some take Aetna (for instance), and some don't. This means the people who need medical care the most simply can't get it. It is outrageous.

At times it feels like we are slaves to the insurance industry, and I personally feel there should be borderless insurance and exceptions made for people with rare diseases. It's frustrating that some (probably most) insurance providers deny tremor-reducing neurotoxins as "cosmetic," making it difficult to find a physician who will purchase the medication and battle the insurance companies for reimbursement. If only those compassionless decision-makers could walk in my shoes for a day… we'd see a change in the insurance industry… pronto!

CHAPTER 13
DISNEY WORLD HONEYMOON AND A CRUISE

Life is an adventure. Try doing it with CMT.
~Frank Creswell

A year after my second divorce, I started thinking about dating again. I wondered if there was a special someone out there to communicate with and share the "rollercoaster" of life. I was a little afraid since I hadn't been in the dating world for several years. I wasn't sure what to expect—something I share in common with anyone new to the modern dating scene, but complicated somewhat by my condition.

I wanted to be honest and upfront with people about CMT so they would not be shocked when they met me. I tried online dating so that I wouldn't meet anyone in person right away. This was good, but also had a downside. They sounded interested until the whole Muscular Dystrophy/CMT information was brought up, then most seemed to disappear. They never told me why, but I knew.

I had been out on several dates with different guys, but none I would consider serious. In this area of Texas, most of the guys did not seem to want a serious relationship like they claimed. A few I dated understood my condition but only took me out once or twice, and that was it. After that, they wouldn't call. I just figured they couldn't deal with it, even when they said it was fine. Maybe they only wanted to play games. That was not what I was looking for.

I was by no means ready to be married again, but I wanted a special person to share things with. I assumed there had to be a few good men out there that could accept something like CMT and were willing to get to know me and not judge me on my disability—it would just take time. I know God had someone in mind for me; I just didn't know who yet. The person would have to be a special, understanding man to handle the "CMT way of life."

Along Came Frank

Honestly, I was somewhat gun-shy going into a new relationship. It took a man like Frank to break down the walls I had built up—a sweet, kind and hardworking man who wanted nothing more than to be with me. He bore the battle scars of life just like I did, and there was something comfortable about being with him.

Aside from being handsome, I noticed right away that Frank is a loyal type of person. From the time we started dating, his head has been on swivel—he looks out for me, and for once in my adult life, I felt like someone's priority—what a wonderful feeling!

Frank just "gets" me. He tip-toed into my family and quietly attached himself. He's stuck to my side ever since, which makes it easy for me to stick by him as well. After a long engagement, we had a little country wedding and a reception at a restaurant. We almost had to postpone it due to Frank's emergency gall bladder surgery. At the end of the dinner after the ceremony, he was ready to get home and get back into his sweats! The jeans were bothering his drain tubes.

Home, by the way, is the house I built with my first husband. I'm now there with Frank, who wasn't too sure he wanted to move in, at least at first. It was a practical decision, but I imagine one day we'll move into a new place and start fresh. Selling the house won't be easy, however, because my parents put up an awkwardly-placed privacy fence, which I cannot stand. It's hard to get in and out of the garage, and we have to back up on the grass to get turned around if we are parked in the driveway. I have asked to have it taken down, but my dad keeps refusing. The memories we've made in the house more than make up for it.

We kept the theme of "fun" going during our Disney World honeymoon, which I worried would be too tiring for Frank. I didn't want him to overdo it. But this was the first vacation he had ever taken in his whole life. Disney World was his pick because his grandma had gone many years prior and brought him a special gift—a flipbook that he still cherishes to this day. Plus, we had made reservations in advance and didn't want to lose our deposit. We decided to drive to Florida despite his post-op status.

I love Disney World. It brought back such fond memories of vacations with Ryan when he was little, but also a twinge of sadness. Ryan had always wanted to revisit Disney World, but as a single mom, I could never afford it.

I used to rave about Disney World's disability accommodations and looked forward to an easy-going vacation. We knew we'd be on the run a lot of the time, trying to fit everything in. So imagine my surprise when we discovered that many things had changed. It was more difficult to navigate the parks. I didn't like that, and neither did Frank. In hindsight, we probably should have chosen a venue that was a bit more leisurely and allowed more "together time." But we made some great memories as we started our new life as a married couple.

Oh, we had fun on the rides! At times I shouted out, "This one's for you, Ryan," mainly on the fast roller coasters because those were his favorites, and mine too. Frank, not so much. One night in our hotel room, I caught him playing on the hotel's gaming system, roaming around the Florida park and giving himself a virtual tour. I was in the other room and thought I heard Mickey's voice. So when I came out, I asked him if he was playing a game with Mickey. He was as happy as a kid! I thought it was adorable.

Frank was such a trooper. He even mentioned that he's ready for more vacations! Now he's hooked on Disney World too. I appreciate that he wanted to contribute to this book and has done so in the missive below. I feel that it's a raw and honest "take" on our relationship, considering that we are now both dealing with my disease.

***

At the end of September 2019, Frank and I were able to go on a second honeymoon, which doubled as my birthday celebration. I had decided to scatter a small amount of Ryan's ashes in the ocean because he loved to cruise, loved the ocean, and loved to swim. This is one of the reasons I decided to arrange a cruise.

I picked the Carnival Cruise line because Frank is a fan of Guy Fieri from the Food Network, and the internet made it seem that a Guy Fieri restaurant would be on board. However, it was really just part of the pool deck and consisted of burgers with fries. Honestly, I thought the food on the cruise was horrible. I've been on plenty of cruises and hated that Frank's first-ever cruise happened to be that one. I did tell him that if we didn't want to get dressed up for the restaurant, we could go through the buffet line. Unfortunately, the buffet's offerings weren't that great either.

I booked us for an excursion on a bamboo raft in Jamaica through the cruise line. But when Frank and I went to the excursion desk, and they found out I was disabled, they said I shouldn't be on the rocky, uneven terrain and refunded our money. As we got off the boat in Jamaica, it seemed everyone in the world tried to get us to go with them on alternate excursions. One lady stopped us and asked what we wanted to do. We weren't sure but climbed in a van that was very difficult for me because the steps were so steep. Frank and a fellow tourist, who happened to be a nurse, helped me step up into the bus.

A guy told us about a beach stop and other stops and offered to drive us there. We thought it would be a guided-type tour, but he said, "I'll be back at 2 p.m. for you." That's when we realized the driver was just a glorified taxi service. There was no way I could stay at the beach that long without having a clue about the amenities, so the guy agreed to do some sightseeing with us. Once he understood what we really wanted, he said, "Don't worry, I can take you to the rafts where there are some stairs with a handrail." I was happy because this meant Frank and I would get to go on the bamboo rafts after all.

So, off we went on our raft (Frank, the tour guide and me), and we thoroughly enjoyed the river. It was serene and quiet with little-to-no movement. I assumed the total cost would be fifty dollars, but the tour guide charged us separately for the "taxi service" and suggested we use the ATM at the cruise terminal. There was no way I was getting dinged with international ATM fees—I learned that lesson in Grand Cayman, one of our first ports where the ATM fee was added to our bill. It almost cost as much to use the debit card as the price of the bagel, sandwiches and two coffees. I ended up scrounging in my purse and Frank in his wallet, and we settled the bill.

The port in Cozumel was better—we swam with the dolphins! Unfortunately, we were stuck at an entrance with fifteen steps instead of the entrance with a ramp. Still, those dolphins made every step and every penny worth it.

At this point, back on board, I talked to the customer service desk about scattering Ryan's ashes. Two attendants took us to the second deck, the mechanical operations level, so that we were closer to the water. I stood close to the edge and opened the bottle, and couldn't control my emotions as I let the ashes go. I wept, and Frank wiped my tears. He told me later that there were ashes on my cheek, as if Ryan had kissed me goodbye. Frank videoed the moment, and the Captain presented us with a note that described the exact longitude and latitude of our location. It was very meaningful.

I also learned another lesson, and that is to never, ever book the front of a ship. On a cruise, you have to request a handicapped room, and ours was located in the front. In rough seas, it sounded like someone was pounding on our door, although it was just the waves!

Despite some of the aggravations and small inconveniences, all in all, Frank thoroughly enjoyed our celebratory cruise, and I did as well. Having never been on a cruise before, he had nothing to compare our experience to and thought the whole thing was pretty spectacular. I was more disappointed because I knew what it could have been. Regardless, Frank is hooked on cruises now (like he is Disney World), and I can't wait to take him on our next adventure. Hopefully, it will far exceed his expectations, and mine!

Have I mentioned that the biggest problem while cruising and staying in hotel handicapped rooms is counter space? When they try to carve out more room for handrails and such, it seems they do so by sacrificing counter space. It just so happens that handicapped people need counter space too. Is it too much to ask that people with disabilities have well-designed hotel rooms and bathrooms that can accommodate us comfortably and safely? Even public bathrooms need to be more accommodating. It would take collaboration with actual handicapped people to design and construct something that is suitable, but do design engineers and architects take the time to consult with us? Have they thought of including feedback from those of us who actually use the rooms? Sometimes I wonder.

From Frank

To start off, it's unclear whether Dawn truly understands how much I respect and admire her. I doubt I could endure the pain and struggle she has had to deal with over the years, and I've known pain. She is an inspiration and a wonderful helpmate, and my best friend. So, this is a love letter to my wife.

We met online (YES, on a dating site), and she was reluctant to meet in person, probably due to some of the pieces of work she met onlinr in the recent past. Instead, we communicated by phone for a couple of weeks with on-and-off results, most good, some not. There were a few hang-ups, but I decided to take a chance on her. So, I drove down to meet her in the town of Nacogdoches, which was not a far drive for her. I first laid eyes on her at a gas station, of all places. When I arrived, I noticed she was pleasantly short! I say that because I am short as well.

I thought she was nervous because her lip was quivering at that time. I didn't realize it was due to her tremors and told her not to be nervous. I learned later that she wasn't even aware of the lip quiver, which meant she had no idea of how adorable she looked the moment I laid eyes on her. We hit it off pretty well and dined at her favorite Mexican restaurant. She then gave me a quick tour of Nacogdoches. We sat and talked at a park in town for a while that night and had a very enjoyable time. We hugged and parted ways.

Hence started my final love story with the most amazing woman. Short of my mother, she is the strongest woman that I've ever met. My first impressions were that she moved a little jerkily but pretty well. Her optimism was kind of infectious. I then had the privilege of meeting and falling in love with her beautiful dog Mandy, a beautiful black Lab mix. Of course, I'm a dog guy and have been my whole life, so Mandy was a bonus.

Eventually, I met Dawn's son Ryan and then her immediate family. I quickly realized this group was strained, to put it lightly. Dawn got to know my mom as well, and they adore each other. Anytime we can visit her, she treasures her time with us. But I digress.

I fell in love with that special optimism that is so unique to Dawn, and it didn't hurt that she is very attractive and sweet and smart and kind! I've been married FIVE times, so falling in love wasn't at the top of my list. In my defense, I seemed to attract (present company EXCLUDED, of course) the worst sort of women in my past. My relationships were fairly short, and all were bad in one way or another. I tended to find the most messed up people… until now.

Dawn has been the most stable and resolute thing in my life, and this is the happiest I've ever been with anyone. I feel like I was created to be by her side, and after a lifetime of trying with the wrong people, I vowed to show her that not all men were like her past encounters. In-kind, she proved to me that not all women are like the ones I've encountered.

I proposed Christmas 2017 and gave Dawn an early Christmas present, a long wooden sign engraved with "Always kiss me in the morning." This was in response to "Always kiss me good night"—something that Dawn said frequently. I put a sticky note on the sign that said, "Will you?" and used a flat tack to attach a ring. Then I wrapped and wrapped and wrapped the sign, and don't think she's ever unwrapped a gift like that.

I recorded this proposal—Dawn had me turn my phone off and said, "Yes, but it's going to be a long engagement." I slipped the ring on her finger, and it fit pretty well. I was relieved it all went as planned and that she agreed to marry me. But Dawn wasn't kidding when she insisted; we waited quite a while to marry. So, I patiently waited and grew to love her with my whole heart. Every day I was in awe of her tenacity and drive.

Living with someone who has a debilitating disease is no different than living with anyone else. There are just different considerations to, well, consider. Perhaps I am just not wired to look at her disability, but rather at her entire being. I guess I've had so many things happen in my life that it has changed my perception of what is important. I didn't see someone who couldn't do for herself, but someone so determined to make it happen that nothing else mattered.

Dawn's inner beauty shone so brightly, and it was easy to fall in love with her. Regardless of her family situation or her devotion to her son, she made room for me. I knew I was supposed to be with her. I finally knew where I was supposed to be, which was at her side. I immediately became protective of her, which is difficult when a person is as fiercely independent as she is! I am the same way, which means we clash sometimes.

The first time I actually saw her fall, it broke my heart. It brought to mind my dad, who had multiple types of cancer during his last six years of his life. He'd beat one, and another came, and it finally wore out his heart. He died on January 23, 2016, and didn't get to meet Dawn. I so wished he could have finally seen that I found a very good one… my last one.

Since I lost my dad, I wished that Dawn had a better relationship with her father. Not having my dad around any longer, I hunger to hear his voice just one more time. Unfortunately, Dawn now understands that deep sense of loss because her only child passed away on Christmas day, 2018. That kills me, knowing how she loved Ryan. I have no children of my own, so I can't imagine that kind of pain.

He was a good guy, just twenty years old and as driven as his mom. I would call him as headstrong as his mom. She poured everything she had into that boy, so, like every parent, it struck her hard when he bucked back. I've been there. I was a young man once and understand the unquenchable desire to be grown and to be a man. That's what he wanted to be in front of his mom—independent.

All I had to do was look at Dawn's house—it's a testament to her and Ryan and their lives together. It was a tad intimidating to move into this place, and once I moved there, I instinctively knew my place. When Ryan tested his wings and would test his mother, I had the sense to know when to stay quiet, listen and just be present until Dawn asked for help or advice. Only then did I interject my opinion, which was hard as hell for someone as outspoken as me. It was a kinda stroke of luck that Ryan had just moved out of the house around the time I moved in, so he only came home from college on the weekends to do laundry and eat all the food, LOL.

Living out in the middle of nowhere has its advantages and disadvantages. It's hard to find work out here, and no one wants to spend the money to let a trucker go home when you live in the middle of nowhere. Miles are money. I've been a truck driver for twenty-three years. But when I'm home and not driving, Dawn knows she can lean on me for the help around the house. I absolutely don't mind doing anything for her, especially handyman-type chores. I was blessed to be taught by an electrician (my dad) and a carpenter (my grandfather), so I'm quite handy, or at least I think so. And I haven't burnt the house down YET! The house did need some TLC, and I'm glad I can help.

Bless her heart; Dawn still hasn't really figured out how to be a trucker's wife. It's hard, to say the least, and I'm a trucker for a reason. I don't play well with others, never have. Even at an early age, I didn't have many friends, only a few. So, I found that truck driving was a good fit. Being alone doesn't bother me at all, and I felt led to do this for a living. I also feel led to help my community and my country in my service this way by delivering goods without ever getting a "Thank you, driver." But Dawn is beginning to understand how important the job is. The stress of the job has a tendency to make me a little rough around the edges. I'm a handful and can be a hard ass. I'm sure she will agree! But she is and will continue to be my world until I breathe no more. She has taught me through her disease to be a more compassionate, loving, understanding and generous person. That being said, she would most likely say that she'd like to see these traits become more visible in me! She says I grumble too much. And I do.

I've grown pessimistic in my old age, but Dawn has a way of making the mundane things of life not seem so relevant. However, I'm also seeing this disease take its toll on her emotions. In public, Dawn is a different person, always worried about how people look at her and how they perceive her. Personally, I don't worry about what people think, but that's just me, being short and growing up next to a 6'8" father. It toughened me up… emotionally, that is.

I do wish a little of me in that respect would rub off on her, but her reaction is due to a lifetime of ridicule and challenges. Life is just harder for her in some regards, but I'm here for her and am so proud to be her husband. As a final word, I would like to pass along a small bit of encouragement to others dealing with a loved one with this disease: You can't change it or fix it, so just be there for them in any way possible. And always remember to just breathe… and pray.

Incredible with my AFOs on

Frank's first visit to Magic Kingdom

Epcot Center

Enjoying Epcot

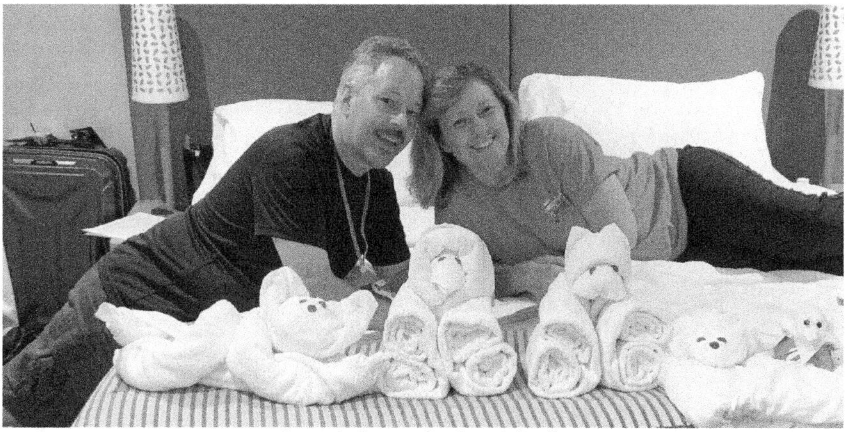

Our whole towel origami family

River raft ride in Jamaica, making the walk down to it in my Dynamic Braces

CHAPTER 14
THE GOODNESS IN GRIEF

God gave us memory so that we might have roses in December.
~James M. Barrie

I made stroganoff the other night, a meal I taught Ryan how to make before he left home. I can't tell you how many times I got a phone call or text asking:

"Mom, how do you make stroganoff again?"

"Ryan, write this down, please!" I reminded him for the umpteenth time.

Then I'd get another call later, or Frank would get a text asking what's in stroganoff.

That Ryan. Now I'd gladly give him the stroganoff recipe a gazillion times if only he was here. So many times, I pick up the phone to call him, even after a year of his passing. It's difficult, so difficult.

My first deep experience with loss takes me back to Rocky, the beloved horse I mentioned in previous chapters. I was seven when I got him, and he retired from giving lessons at the age of thirty-one. Every time I went to the barn, he stood quietly and offered his neck for a big hug, or would let me hold on to steady myself while walking to the barn. Rocky was more than just an animal to me; he was my best friend and kept my spirit alive through many difficult times. My two other quarter horses took over the lessons, but they could never replace the kindness and gentleness that Rocky offered to everyone.

Rocky died in 2014 at the age of thirty-four—a good long life. I did a write-up about my relationship with him in his scrapbook, and my mother contributed one as well, a eulogy of sorts:

Rocky has been the best horse that I've ever known. He has been my companion and friend for twenty-plus years. I don't know what I would have done without him in my life. Rocky always listened without any complaints and could always make me feel better when I was down. He has taken me to many places that I would have never been able to go on my own. He could always make me laugh when he would see me coming with a carrot because he would start saying, "Yes, I want that" by nodding his head up and down.

We share a special bond that no other horse can replace. I sometimes think he is part human since he will do something I want before I ask for it. Now at age twenty-six, he is still willing to do whatever I ask, but he does enjoy longer days being left out to graze. We talk more now than we ride, and his soft, gentle eyes still tell me that he is listening. This is true love from a horse. Thank you for all your love and companionship, Rocky. Love ~ Dawn Johnson

My mother wrote:

I remember getting up early on show mornings and eating my apple on the way to the barn. Upon arriving at the barn, I would give you the leftover apple. You sure enjoyed it. You have helped Dawn through her teenage years and right through womanhood and motherhood, and I want to thank you for that. You watched over her, and you will always hold a special place in my heart. There will never be another Rocky. We have a lot of good memories of horse shows and other events with you. ~ Kathy Johnson

I titled this chapter "The Goodness in Grief" because we all must grieve at some point in our lives, and we can all identify the positives that come out of it. That may sound counterintuitive at first, but it's true. When I was diagnosed with CMT in my childhood, I went through a period of grief. However, I arrived at a state of mind called "acceptance." This is the life God has given me, and I am thankful for every day of it. It's a challenging life, but it has taught me to be a super strong and super compassionate woman.

As huge as the loss of Rocky was, as well as several other horses, it in no way prepared me for the loss of Ryan. When my firstborn and only son died, I experienced a grief like no other. There are just not adequate words to describe that plummeting, endless spiral of mourning. And yet, I was able to adjust. I was able to equip myself to adjust by finding online support groups, leaning on my family, and relying on Frank for comfort. Most of all, it strengthened my relationship with the Lord. I realize that for unbelievers, it is difficult to comprehend this phenomenon.

I am still processing the grief over the death of Ryan and dreaded the holidays as they approached once again. I am still wrapping my head around the one-year anniversary of my new role as the mother of an angel. I would much rather be the mother of a living, breathing son. Life will never be the same, but I think that I've been dealing with all the grief pretty well. There is a goodness in the grief journey when we are able to honor our lost loved ones and memorialize what they meant to us. We can derive comfort and strength in God, who has a greater plan and promised us a way forward. We can find ways to celebrate the time given to us with loved ones. We can honor them by living life as they would want us to.

Loss of My Son and a Funeral

It's painful to recall the morning I lost Ryan, but want to commemorate his passing and how we memorialized him. I went to Ryan's room on Christmas morning to wake him up, but I could not get him to respond. I yelled for Frank as the panic kicked in, and then called Ryan's father, who said he'd call me back after seeing if he could leave work. He did call back to say he was on his way and was in an absolute rage. Frank answered the phone and got a violent earful, unfortunately. He handed the phone over to me after I had calmed down enough to speak.

Frank called 911. A mutual friend who happened to be a police detective in Nacogdoches came over immediately and offered support. Soon half the community was in my yard and living room, including Ryan's paternal family. My mother came immediately; I thought she'd hug me, but instead, she walked around the house, not knowing what to do. She was in shock. We were all in shock. The EMT's arrived and went through Ryan's bags, looking for his identification. I didn't want them to take any of his things... they ended up with his driver's license, and we kept his wallet.

I remember my mom tapped me on the shoulder and told me the names of the two funeral homes in town. In hindsight, I think she was trying to distract me, so I would not see my son's body being wheeled out of my home. The whole thing left us stunned. This was Christmas Day, Ryan's favorite holiday. He was supposed to be opening gifts, not being loaded into an ambulance. Why did he have to die on this day? Why did a twenty-year-old have to die at all?

I had to take my medicine but hadn't eaten. Frank insisted I eat something to coat my stomach, so he made some toast. Actually, he burned the toast. For some reason, I thought this was humorous and ate the toast anyway. I was going through such a blur of emotions. I remember vacillating between denial and horror, knowing my son was with the Lord, yet unable to process the loss.

Wow. All I can say is that I have a whole new appreciation for mothers who have lost children and face the prospect of a funeral service. People are in no emotional shape to handle the details, but there isn't a choice. I pushed forward in a haze, determined to give my son a proper service. But first, an autopsy had to be performed. The results of the tests and cause of death didn't arrive until after the funeral. In the meantime, I planned the service, focusing on what I knew Ryan would want.

What a surprise I got when his father informed me that Ryan had previously given him a limited power of attorney. Apparently, they had conversed about what to do if Ryan was ever in a car accident or otherwise died, never dreaming that Ryan would lose his life to undiagnosed lymphocytic myocarditis at such an early age. Since Ryan was a conservative young man with well-formed political opinions, he had a favorite 2020 Trump sweatshirt. We honored his wishes by having him wear this particular sweatshirt in addition to his blue jeans, his glasses and his shoes and braces.

Honestly, Ryan was not fond of suits, and I didn't care what Ryan wore. It wasn't worth wasting one more minute of my energy on convention or keeping up appearances. It was more important that his outfit captures the essence of what he stood for; in my heart, I felt like he was smiling down on us from above, tickled that his funeral attire was everything he'd wear during a typical day.

His braces were later donated to Sherrie Anderson, CP, LPO, of Anderson Orthopedics and Prosthetics, who made Ryan's first ankle supports. She does such good work for her clients as well as people in the mission field. Ryan's braces became a gift to Africa. I knew Ryan would want to donate his body for research, specifically CMTA research, but was informed by the funeral home that this was not possible since the autopsy took too long. Therefore, we later had him cremated.

In lieu of flowers, I asked for donations to be made in Ryan's honor at the Charcot-Marie-Tooth Association. A viewing was scheduled for 2 p.m. on Sunday, December 30, 2018, with a service to follow at 3 p.m. at Cason Monk Funeral Home in Nacogdoches. For those who weren't able to make it, I shared the program on social media.

FUNERAL SERVICES
3:00 PM, Sunday, December 30, 2018
Cason Monk-Metcalf Sunset Chapel
Nacogdoches, Texas

OFFICIATING
Rev. Michael Parks

IN MEMORY OF
Ryan William Schaeffer
July 19, 1998 ~ December 25, 2018

Included in the program were:

For God so loved the world,
That He gave his only begotten
Son, the whosoever believeth
In Him should not perish, but
Have everlasting life.
JOHN 3:16

The Lord is my shepherd;
I shall not want.
He maketh me to lie down
In green pastures;
He leadeth me beside still waters.
He restoreth my soul;
He leadeth me in the paths
Of righteousness for His Name's sake
Yea, though I walk through the valley
Of the shadow of death,
I will fear no evil;
For thou art with me;
They rod and Thy staff
They comfort me;
Thou prepares a table before me
In the presence of mine enemies;
Thou annointest my head with oil,
My cup runneth over.
Surely goodness and mercy
Shall follow me all the days of my life,
And I will dwell in the house of the Lord, forever.
PSALM 23

As for coordinating the funeral service itself, which fell on a Sunday, the dynamics between his father and me didn't make it easy. I had selected music for the funeral and coordinated it with the pastor's notes, so the music would cue at appropriate intervals. My former sister-in-law intervened and produced a different rendition of the music, which annoyed me to no end. That was not the way Ryan would want it to be—his favorite songs were excluded. My pastor was very upset that none of the music we wanted to play was actually played.

We arrived early for the family viewing so we could be the only ones present. As I viewed the casket from the front pew, I just could not go up to view Ryan's body. I wasn't ready and sat there a few minutes as the video played, compiled of Ryan's photos through all the stages in his life. I went to the ladies' room and came back out to a flood of people. My dad was in a corner with his walker, standing next to my mom. I just stood there as people came up to me from every direction. Frank's mother came up and hugged me.

Then we were informed it was time to be seated. As I walked toward my seat, someone said, "Hey, Dawn." It was one of the boys who had bullied Ryan; it just so happened that Ryan stood up to him, defended himself, and ultimately beat up the bully. The boy wanted to give me his condolences, which I thought was profound and very heartwarming. It made me more aware of Ryan's role as a CMT ambassador—someone who others could relate to and learn from. A few other people arrived that I didn't really expect to see, like people I worked out with at the women's gym. They knew Ryan because he played video games while he waited for me.

People stood and spoke. The first eulogy was given by a good friend of Ryan's who was really hit hard by the loss. She was younger than him, but their humor went hand in hand. She managed to speak through many tears. His godmother, Amy Anderson Gerlach, gave her eulogy as well. Even though we aren't Catholic, I chose her to be there for Ryan in case anything happened to either his father or me. She was very close to Ryan and told a touching story of how he used to take her hair clips and try to put them in his hair when she visited. She lived in New Jersey and later Wisconsin, but made a yearly visit. Their birthdays were four days apart. He absolutely loved her and their time spent together. When we'd take her to the airport, he always moved to her seat on the drive home and commented that the seatbelt smelled like her. Amy and I are still in shock about losing him and can't believe he's gone. We often talk about him and all the good times we had together.

Jammie, his aunt from the other side, eulogized Ryan as well. She recalled that they were always close, and she loved it when they made road trips with the music blaring as they sang. Once everyone had said their goodbyes to Ryan, a few really close friends stayed behind and asked me to call if I needed anything. One of my friends sat with me for a while—I hadn't seen her for a time, and our boys grew up together. "I just can't believe it," she said, trying to console me. I was in tears the whole time. One friend wanted to go to view Ryan, but not by herself. I told her I'd go with her while Frank went outside to give Ryan's dad some of Ryan's things, including the Christmas presents he had given Ryan.

Then Ryan's father asked me what we planned to do with his truck. What? This was such an inappropriate question, considering Ryan didn't own it; my parents owned it. To bring it up at our son's funeral was not appreciated, but worse, he asked for Ryan's watch and phone. I told him we could talk about it later. I left to go to the restroom while Frank was still in the sanctuary. Ryan's dad literally turned around and said, "There is nothing left here for me anymore," while his son was still lying right in front of him in the casket. I can't believe he was so insensitive. I guess I can, but I was the last one standing by my son's side; I didn't want to have to say goodbye. Still thinking about everything today, my eyes tear up.

Warm Tributes for Ryan

It was a very nice service on a rainy, cold afternoon that honored my son well. Ryan's best friend since second grade came; he's in the military and took leave to tell Ryan goodbye. The United States flag and the Army flag stood on each side of the casket—Ryan was such a patriotic young man.

About half of the attendees came to my house for refreshments, and half went to my parents' home. Our wonderful friend Linda Perkins made a lot of the food for the funeral and kept bringing food for a few days after the funeral because we had so many family members in. I appreciated her efforts and kindness so much.

Later the comments from friends on social media flooded in, some sweet, some heart-wrenching, and some humorous—and I felt it was appropriate to share a few below from our family and Ryan's friends.

Handsome Ryan Schaeffer, you will be forever missed by everyone! So sorry for your loss at this sad time Dawn Johnson and family! Sending hugs and comforting prayers to everyone! I will miss you Sweet Ryan, till we meet again!

My heart is so broken right now to learn of a beloved friend who went to see Jesus this Christmas morning. Ryan, I will miss your loving smile and laugh so much, but I know I will see you again someday I know it's not a goodbye for now but a see you later soon my friend love always.

What a wonderful tribute to Ryan. Keeping you in my prayers.

Sorry I did not get a chance to speak or hug you. No words I can say can ease your loss or pain you feel in your heart. You raised a fine young man. Love you.

It was a beautiful service.

I'm sorry I didn't make it to the service. I was one of Ryan's instructors at TSTC. I was so saddened to hear he had passed. He was a wonderful young man with a huge heart and a smile to match it. I'm glad I was able to know him.

Prayers are with you!!

I am so sorry for your loss.

Dawn, thank you for sharing this with us. I couldn't attend because I was out of town. He was a great kid! Always smiling! Praying for you and your family!

Blessed to have known & taught Ryan, and I counted him as a friend. The service was beautiful, and I think Ryan was happy to see all the loving, familiar faces there to celebrate him.

Continued prayers and hugs for you and your family.

My heart breaks for you. May you be blessed with the Lord's Peace.

Wanted to attend his service. He's a friend of mine. I know one of his wishes was to give his mother a cake I made before. I still want to give his mother the cake he knew she would love. Please contact me, my heart aches that he didn't make arrangements on a date to pick up a gift he wanted to give his mother. I work at Kroger in Marshall, TX.

I hope that you are hanging in there so far. I pray for you Dawn to get through all of this. I really am so upset that this happened to you. May the lord be with you to help Guide you and comfort you.

Ryan Schaeffer, today was hard. Today was VERY hard to say a final goodbye to someone like you. You were the most dearest friend of all. All I can think of those few words you said to me last we saw one another... "I'm glad we met" with the most biggest grin! I'm so sad that you are gone. I needed you but God needed you the most. I'm happy for the fact that you had got the chance to see our Father in Heaven on Christmas day...your favorite time of the year! We may not cross paths for a while but will soon. Save me a spot up above.

I couldn't attend the funeral today. I couldn't stop thinking about how much I'm going to miss him.

Praying for you. Love you.

Love this pic of us. Fun memories and your sweet smile. Miss you dearly, nephew.

It is SO hard to lose someone you held dear. Your memories will be always in your heart.

He was just too young.

I feel so sad for all of you! I do not know your sister and her family, but please give them my condolences.

We will miss Ryan greatly at ABC. What a sweet guy.

***

The funeral director kindly provided a book from the service filled with remembrances from friends and family as well. Below I share some of their wonderful comments.

June 25, 2011 So glad you were able to be part of our wedding day. We love you and take comfort in knowing you live on in our hearts and memories. Love always, Andrew and Amy Gerlach

I didn't know Ryan long, but I often heard of him and his great accomplishments in his short life. I think when someone passes to young, we must look at their quality of life and not their quantity of life. We can't explain why God lets things happen, and we'll never figure out the true reason, but we must trust and have faith. And what I know about Ryan is that he'll be watching all his family, friends and those so special in his life from this day forward. He has moved to a place where there is no pain, no suffering, no sickness, no disabilities and no sadness, and we should all take comfort in that. As I looked through the many photos today I'm reminded what a happy young man he was. He chose to see the best in people and in life, and he made the most out of his. I know when those close to him think of him, although they are sad, they smile because he brought happiness to all of them. And isn't that a great gift we can all give others? Everyone who thinks of him will remember the great things he meant to them, the fantastic times they spend with them and the positive inspiration he always was. God bless Ryan and his family and friends he left behind, for some day we will all see him again and once again smile and laugh and catch up on old times. God Bless! ~ John Krueger

Ryan, I didn't know you very well, however your everyday actions tell a lot about your character. I can't seem to remember seeing you without joy written all across your face. You're someone who's ambitions were never out of reach, regardless of how far they were amongst the stars. A part of me looked up to you. ~ Dakota Montgomery

I knew Ryan for a short time but loved him like a son. My daughter Makayla was a friend of his in Douglass. I'm praying for his family and friends to receive the strength, love and the closure that they need in this tragic time. He will be missed deeply!! Love you and will miss you Ryan! ~ Shantel Yates

Ryan, you will never be far from our thoughts. We will always remember watching you grow up into a fine young man. We will always have fond memories of our movie nights when we would have a bowl of ice cream topped with loads of whip cream. We will forever miss you. We love you. ~ Grandpa and Grandma Johnson

I have only met you a few times, you always had a smile on your face. Seemed a very happy person. I will miss that I won't have the chance to know you more. Love, Aunt Bev

I will always remember you, your smile, your laugh, and your willingness to help anybody. I watched you grow up into a fine young man. I will miss you terribly on my visits to Texas. Show those angels in heaven how to fix their computers. Will love you always, Aunt Ruth

I can't think of a single time I ever saw Ryan without a smile on his face here at work… he is the most cheerful person I have ever met. He would come to my desk for a piece of candy and ALWAYS said "I'm sorry… I just want one"… I always laughed and told him that's what the candy is there for and that he could take more than one because we both knew good and well he would be back for more. We recently had our office Christmas party/gift exchange… I will never forget his laughter as he watched everyone open funny "gag" gifts. I speak confidently when I say ALL of Ryan's ABC Family will miss Ryan dearly. What a tremendous loss for us all. ~ Deepest Sympathy, Ariana Moore

I will miss you everyday of my life, I remember so well when you were born, watched you grow up and become a man. You worked hard to become who you are today. When you were in grammar school you made me a turkey out of a brown paper bag, painted construction paper in different colors for the tail. It is a little battered after all these years but it has always had a special place on my table every Thanksgiving. Now, it takes on new meaning. I love you Ryan, will miss you terribly but I believe we will meet again someday. Go rest high on that mountain. ~ Aunt Janece

I'm sending all my thoughts and sympathy to Ryan's family and friends. I wish for his mama the peace that is found through the happy memories she holds of Ryan. ~ Mitzi Easley

Ryan, many thanks for the lessons you gave me on flying Drones. Now you are flying even higher than our Drones. Even though our time together was very short, I will miss you. Petrina and I extend our deepest sympathy and best wishes to your extended family. ~ Terry Bradunas

I haven't seen Ryan in a long time but I know how much his mama loved him. My heart breaks for you, Dawn and your family. I know firsthand how it feels to lose a child. Much hugs and prayers for you and your family. ~ Lauren Gaudette

I remember the time Ryan came to New Jersey and visited our NJ office. He had such a big personality and an even bigger smile. He had many jokes to tell and we all enjoyed his visit. My heart breaks for his family with such a great loss. Dawn, may all the fond memories and many photos of Ryan with his big smile bring you comfort during this most difficult time. Our deepest condolences to the Johnson and Schaeffer families and all the extended family and friends that knew Ryan. May he Rest in Peace. ~ Helen & Kevin Sochacki

Love our boy so much. His beautiful smile would light up a room. Ryan's big heart loved so much. I will miss his hugs. And his big laughter. It would make you laugh so hard your belly would hurt. I wish we had more time together. I can't wait to be dancing with you at the heavenly party. I will miss you everyday, every hour, every minute until I see you again. Tell Uncle David we miss him also. I don't want to say goodbye. I love you always, your Aunt Misty.

I met Ryan when he was in my daycare room. He was such a sweet boy. He has the sweetest smile/ bright eyes and lit the whole room. ~ Tamika Ward

R.I.P. Ryan! I can't believe this happened and so suddenly too! I wish I could have gotten to know you better when I moved closer to the family. I love you cousin! ~ Tricia Bottema

I met this sweet boy at Faith Bridge Church always had a smile on his face full of love for everyone. I watched him grow up into a man standing behind my stylist chair. Always loving to laugh and have a good time. He was a shining light in the darkness I say. Always laughing, helping, smiling, and always standing up for what was right, always taking up for his love for our country leaders, our president and the American soldiers, he loved his family very much. He was always striving to do better. It breaks my heart that he is not still here with us. I will miss his smile and loving soul so very much Ryan until we meet again my friend. RIP Ryan. I will see you again, love. ~ Shante Brewer

You were the light in your mother's life and you always will be. Be at peace in heaven until the day you may embrace once more. ~ Cecy Robson

Ryan! I am so glad you were a part of mine and Mia's life! You always had us laughing. You were my margarita/ daiquiri buddy! You were the first one to know David and I would end up married and you even got to be there when we did the thing, the memorable River Trip 2016! You will be so so so missed! ~ Erin Ward

Ryan… my heart hurts that Mackenzie will never be able to hear your amazing, hilarious laugh. I'll never forget all the summers all of us cousins laughed until we cried and playing cards around the table, I know you cheated sometimes but I'll let it go this one time lol. I'll miss you so much. I love you cousin, save a seat for me. ~ Kylie Lewis

Ryan, you lit up any room that you walked into. Your laugh and incredible smile was infectious, no one could stay sad or angry with you around. You will be missed more than I can describe. I thank God that He let us share you, even though it was such a short time. RIP my dear friend and nephew in my heart. ~ Mary Amerson

A Balloon Tribute

As Ryan's birthday in July approached, I looked on a grieving moms' site about how people handle the first birthday post-loss. I wanted Chinese lanterns, but that was impractical. So, a balloon release was the next best thing. Red was Ryan's favorite color, which inspired the color of the balloons, a festive, bright color that would stand out against the blue sky and white clouds.

The day fell on a Friday, and I admit my feelings were conflicted all week, leading up to the celebration. The raw pain was combined with excitement as I coordinated the outdoor event. Friends and family showed up at the school parking lot, and I held it together as the sky filled with red balloons floating heavenward. It was a beautiful moment. There were many tears shed. I shed tears, too. I missed him so much, and he was so excited about this birthday, to finally be 21! We all hugged one another before leaving this perfect memorial.

Ryan's best friend in San Diego and other people in remote locations released red balloons simultaneously, which made the tribute so extraordinary and special.

After the ceremony, Frank and I went to a cafe and ordered chocolate cake and quesadillas (both Ryan's favorites). We purchased a to-go order and went home, and as Frank lifted his fork full of cake, he said, "This is for you!" This was not the best thing for Frank to eat because he's diabetic, but he did it for Ryan. Then I was emotionally spent. I had done everything I could to keep my son's memory alive. Perhaps Ryan was somehow aware of what we were up to, and if so, I'm sure he got a kick out of it.

The one word that comes to mind is "bittersweet," for the celebration was fun but also poignant. My beloved son deserved no less.

My Father

Grief also allows us to sort out a tangled twist of emotions and put any negative thoughts into context. This brings me to the topic of my father, who was (surprisingly) at the balloon release. Dad was born in 1942 and had a complex relationship with Ryan. I wonder if he regrets how things ended between him and his grandson.

They had a big blowout fight a couple of months before Christmas, mostly based on politics and misperceived meaning, and later on misconstrued text messages. Ryan was incensed that my dad pulled my mom into the mess and said so in the strongest terms. Ryan, who was understandably hurt and upset, sent me screenshots. Thus, he pulled me into the drama as well, but I simply encouraged him to stand by his beliefs.

I have to admit that I admired Ryan's ability to vocalize his feelings, which is something I struggled with when it came to my dad. Ryan was a lot like me when it came to tenacity and stubbornness, but also was one generation removed from my upbringing. This gave him a sense of unbridled freedom to defend himself in family matters.

On Christmas Day, when Ryan died, Dad came over and seemed mentally ill in addition to his physical ailments—colon cancer (which he beat), breathing issues, and being kept alive because my mom waits on him hand and foot. She spends hours rubbing his legs to help the swelling, makes sure he gets his medicine on time, and much more. She has always been a very devoted and patient wife.

Dad is a hard person to "know" and is a harsh critic, as I've mentioned before, so I wasn't sure what to expect as he entered my house. He hardly ever came over; everything had to be done on his own turf. Things started off okay. He said, "We should never have to lose a child," which I wholeheartedly agreed with.

But then he said, "I just never really knew Ryan."

This struck me the wrong way, as if he was blaming Ryan for not knowing him. What the heck? After all, Grandpa was the mature adult in their relationship. Ryan had been alive for two decades—definitely time enough for my father to be involved and "know" his grandson.

I was livid but bit my tongue as usual. In my mind, however, I thought, *It's your own fault, Dad.* Then I prayed, *Lord, please just let this man be quiet and give me a hug.*

It was an emotional ordeal for me, and perhaps for my dad as well. Suffice it to say, I didn't get the hug and was relieved when my dad left my house.

***

I have mentioned my half-sister, who was born to Dad and his first wife, but I only became aware that I had a mystery half-brother after my first divorce, around 2014. This half-brother contacted my dad after growing up elsewhere. My dad wasn't aware of his existence. He looks like our father, and the mannerisms are identical, but they have two totally different types of temper.

I was asked, "Do you want to meet him?" I knew nothing about this new family member, but of course, I wanted to meet him. In fact, (in a strange way) I had a sense of grief that we didn't know him earlier—all those missed moments. But it also dredged up a different kind of grief in a flashback moment. I recalled my dad telling my first husband that he wished I was a boy and that he finally had a son because of our marriage. It made me feel as if I had no meaning in his life. It was an awful thing to hear.

Thankfully, I get along with my brother. He helps me when I need it, and he tries to do the right thing when it comes to the care of his horses, although he is still learning what horses need. I try to give him advice when I can. He says cows are so much easier to handle, and they are, but I like taking care of horses so much more.

Both Mom and Dad think my half-brother is great and awesome. He's basically taken over the business, although my cousin and her husband moved here from Nevada to be the business "bosses" and supervise to make sure everything gets done. That's changed now.

The bottom line is that I have nieces and nephews to love, thanks to my two half-siblings, and appreciate our presence in each other's lives.

***

This brings me to the topic of weight and body image. I had to be a certain weight in order to visit my aunt in Texas as a child. My dad weighed me every morning, and when I came home from Texas, I couldn't be heavier than my initial weight. This meant I had to diet the last couple of weeks I was there because if I came back any heavier, I wouldn't be allowed to go back the following summer. Those were my dad's rules, not my aunt's, because I was chubby.

Yet when Ryan visited my aunt, he ate junk. Spoonfuls of fudge. At the table in the morning, he was asked, "What do you want for breakfast?" and he'd get what he wanted. They also had midnight snacks. Ryan enjoyed his special time with his aunt, who learned the hard way to not overfeed him. She once babysat him when I was on a cruise with his father. He had one too many popsicles before bed; it caused him to throw up on the covers.

So, ever since Ryan was a young boy, his weight didn't seem to be an issue whatsoever, at least to my aunt. My dad was a different story, however. He sprung an exercise regimen on Ryan, one that was ineffective and caused resentment. I will always hold Ryan in my heart as a larger-than-life personality who happened to be extraordinarily courageous. He found the inner courage to speak out against abuse. It's not healthy to hold on to the abuse or bury it, and Ryan was so good at addressing his grandfather's behavior. He stood up to him.

For instance, Ryan and my father went on walks when he was younger. I thought that was great, and Ryan seemed to enjoy it. However, he became less enthused as the months went by. I asked him why, and he said that his grandfather was making him run … and timing him.

What in the world?

Ryan tried with all his might to keep up this regimen, but got discouraged. "Mom," he said, "why can't I just walk with Grandpa? I don't want to run, and I don't like to get timed." He was near tears when he told me this, and I discussed it with Ryan's father. Together we visited my father, taking Ryan with us. My rationale was that even if my dad didn't believe me, he'd have to believe Ryan. Right?

Well, we explained Ryan's concerns and then let Ryan tell my father he didn't want to run. He just wanted to enjoy leisurely strolls with his grandpa in the great outdoors. That went over like a lead balloon. My father was highly insulted and wrote us all off—Ryan included—meaning he stopped speaking to us all. During the times we had to be around each other, like on holidays, it was obvious that dad's relationship with Ryan had become tense and testy.

Ryan didn't stand for it. He was polite, but if pushed, he countered, especially as he got older. If Grandpa made a dig, Ryan dug back. I admired his feistiness, for this wasn't something I can bring myself to do, and I was glad I had produced a young man who stood up for himself. Not that it was easy for Ryan. This eggshell relationship with his grandfather broke Ryan's heart. He used to watch a commercial of a grandfather and grandson; the grandson accidentally stepped on wet cement but didn't get in trouble. I remember distinctly that Ryan would say, "Why can't my grandpa just be a grandpa?"

When Ryan died, that uncomfortable dynamic was still in play. I often wonder how my father feels, knowing he caused a totally preventable chasm that was too late to be bridged. How terribly, terribly sad.

Closing Accounts

Losing a loved one often means wrapping up a thousand little details while still reeling from the loss. Indulge me as I vent, for I had taken care of closing out Ryan's credit cards and bank accounts, etc., and had to explain the circumstances each time: my son was now deceased. Most of the companies were nice enough and closed out the accounts with no problems. However, when it came to dealing with his phone company, AT&T, I never imagined having to explain the situation so many times, over and over again.

I generally would not mention the vendor's name, except I have full documentation for this event and (hopefully) this section will somehow help to improve their service level, or at least give a heads up to readers that this type of incredible annoyance may happen so they can brace for it! In all fairness, at the conclusion of this ordeal, there was a satisfactory result, thanks to the internet and reaching the highest offices at AT&T, as you'll see.

It hurt every time I had to discuss Ryan's death with anyone, let alone total strangers over the phone time and again. I had been reporting his death to AT&T since the beginning of January and gave the phone company everything they asked for. They had no sensitivity. Zero. There was no problem shutting off his number, but getting them to remove the late charges (that really weren't late) was so aggravating and maddening. He was on my account, so I had to get it resolved.

The entire two weeks before my February bill was due, I kept getting notices that my phone service would be shut off. I called the company at least three times in a two-week period to make sure they were still reviewing the past due amount and were not going to shut off my phone. *Why is this so hard?* I asked myself. My son was deceased, so why was it seemingly impossible to remove his charges?

On February 17, I woke up to another message informing me that they were going to shut off my phone and that there would be a reinstatement fee of thirty-five dollars. I spoke to a woman who reassured me that my phone wouldn't be shut off and she was removing the messages so I would not get anymore. I actually raised my voice to her three different times while explaining that my son had died. Her response was, "I'm so sorry," but they never fixed the problem.

I wanted to speak to a supervisor, but he was on another line, "supposedly" helping someone else. I just lost it. How could they be so dumb? Could they not read their own notes? I started my Sunday morning off crying quite a bit, and needless to say, it set a bad tone for the whole day. Being dragged back through the loss all over again was just more than I could bear and made it impossible to move past the sadness.

By the afternoon, I was feeling a little better, but still grieving. I sat in my chair in the living room, looking around at Ryan's smiling face in all the pictures. These images surrounded me and helped. That is how I want to remember him. I wanted to grieve him happily and celebrate the good times rather than fight with people about bills regarding my dead son.

On February 18, I received yet another message that I needed to pay or my phone would be shut off. I was just pissed now but had to keep my cool because I was dealing with these people while I was at work. When I first called and asked for a supervisor, I got through right away, but she hung up the line, and I never heard back. They had my number and could have called me back. I waited until I had another cup of coffee in me and called them again.

This time, it took some time for them to pass me to a supervisor, only to find out that he wasn't a supervisor. I was talking to someone in a different department about closing accounts, which I had already done with Ryan's phone. Once again, I had to explain everything and use the "deceased" word that I was really not liking at that point. I was reassured, once again, that it all would be taken care of. Then I was put on hold so he could look into it further. He came back on the line to reassure me that he was still there and would be back to me in just a few minutes, but then the phone line went dead.

Once again, no callback. I refused to call them back after all of that because I could not stand the notion of telling the whole story again, especially while I was at work. *I will switch carriers if I have to!* I thought to myself. I was one angry customer and a hurting mother on top of it all. Sheesh!

Then—you guessed it—I received another phone call from AT&T about my past due amount! They gave me another phone number to call, but I still could not get past the representatives. I was so mad. No one seemed to have made a note that my son had died, and that was why I had to keep telling each person what had happened. I wanted to scream and cry at the same time.

I kept asking for a manager or supervisor, but all they said was, "Can I get your phone number? We will call you back." I told them no, I wanted to speak with someone NOW! This seemed to fluster them. I just wanted it resolved, but then the representative couldn't even locate the correct case number! Double sheesh!

I finally searched the internet until I found a contact number for the CEO of AT&T and sent an email. Well, guess who got a call the next morning? Yes, me, from the CEO's righthand man. He asked if I was the one who emailed the CEO, and I said, "Absolutely." He was very apologetic and credited my whole bill, and I owed nothing until the next month.

Thank you, Jesus! Thank you for your help with the email information. I think I still would have been going around in circles if it wasn't for the Lord's help and the help of the CEO's assistant. Of course, there is a lesson in all of this. As traumatizing as it was, it proved once again that persistence pays off. It also proved that sometimes we have to do extra research and find the decision-makers who oversee operations, and appeal to them to sort out dilemmas.

So although I have just raked AT&T over the coals, I appreciate that the CEO, through his assistant, cared enough to get involved. Thank you, AT&T, for ultimately resolving an extremely miserable situation. Now perhaps they'll make a donation toward CMT research. That would be the icing on the cake.

Rocky and Ryan graced the cover of our Christmas card.

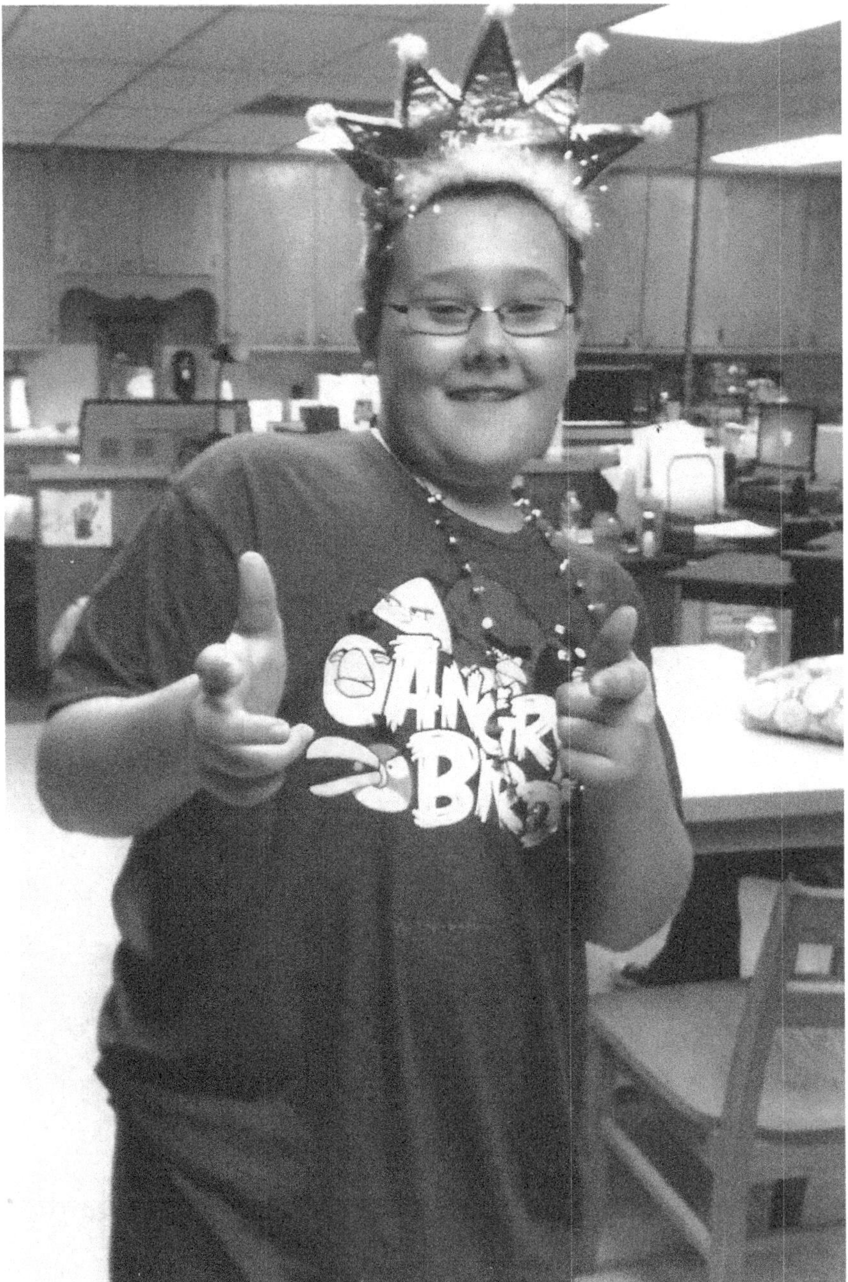

Celebrating the holidays at school

4C • The Daily Sentinel • Wednesday, April 20, 2016

STUDENT PROFILE

Ryan Schaeffer

Douglass High School

Grade: 12

Favorite subject in school: Business Management

What I do to relax: Play on my computer or watch TV.

My most embarrassing moment at school: When I got hit with a dimple ball in P.E.

Something I can't live without: My TV or phone

My favorite move: American Sniper

My favorite food: Pizza

The song I listen to the most is: Dazed and Confused

The text message I send the most: What's up

One day, I hope to visit: England

My friends say I am: Smart

After school I usually: Work-out and then relax

Next summer I would love to: Have as much fun as I can on my summer break before I go off to college.

My birthday dinner with my favorite son and other family and friends

Ryan always made shopping fun!

Right after a hair cut wearing his new shirt that shows exactly what he stood for

Enjoying our ride to Rascal Flatts concert. Ryan always wanted to see them, and I'm so glad I got to take him. We had a great time.

Mexican celebration for his 19th birthday

Ryan's friends brought in this huge cowboy hat for his 20th birthday and made him wear it from dessert until we left.

Douglass Independent School District
Scholarship Fund

With
Warmest Thoughts
And
Appreciation

To Honor Ryan Schaeffer
A donation has been made to the
Douglass Independent School District
Scholarship Fund by
DOUGLASS CLASS OF 2016

Collage of favorite senior photos

Ryan with his cousin Mark (See Chapter 1), whom he talked with for hours about computers when he would visit us in Texas

CHAPTER 15
ASKING FOR HELP

There are only four kinds of people in the world. Those who have been caregivers. Those who are currently caregivers. Those who will be caregivers, and those who will need a caregiver.
~ Rosalyn Carter

As a person with CMT, I value as much independence as I can muster. It's extremely hard for me to ask others for help. Call it ingrained pride, a sense of dignity, a need for self-reliance, or resistance to being perceived as a burden—the bottom line is that I have avoided, whenever possible, requesting assistance from friends and family. Sure, I've relied on the medical community for many years, but they are paid for their services. It's very different to lean on loved ones and trusted friends who have their own lives to manage and are helping me out of the goodness of their hearts.

So, how do we gracefully reach out for help? It has a lot to do with our mindsets. I think the quote leading this chapter by Rosalyn Carter articulates it beautifully: "There are only four kinds of people in the world. Those who have been caregivers. Those who are currently caregivers. Those who will be caregivers, and those who will need a caregiver." With this perspective, I acknowledge my limitations and appreciate those who assist in my day-to-day functions, which is basically inevitable due to the progressive nature of CMT.

In other words, I have reluctantly accepted the fact that I do need help. Once I embraced that notion, it was wonderful to realize that people care about my well-being and don't mind assisting me at all. Yes, the kindness of good people is a gift, and accepting that gift is beneficial to all involved.

If you are a caregiver or partner of someone with CMT, this chapter might be extremely useful. It's not like a manual exists to prep caregivers for this role, so I'm sharing a personal few observations that can help, or at least point people in the right direction.

Cleaning Around the House

I've mentioned the difficulties of cleaning my house; the bathrooms and floors are an extreme challenge. I can still dust and manage to wrangle the vacuum, but mopping and deep cleaning are cumbersome and even dangerous. When budgets are tight, and it isn't possible to hire a cleaning service, the act of a friend or family member who steps in to mop for me is such a Godsend. Seriously, if you are visiting a friend with a disability, ask where he or she keeps the mop and jump in. Don't ask "if" you can help, but take the lead with the full knowledge that this means the world to someone with CMT, especially.

Of course, everyone's disability is unique. Some may not be able to vacuum or dust at all. Others may need help with laundry, changing sheets and making beds. I think a good rule of thumb is: if it's labor-intensive for an able-bodied person, it's doubly or triply labor-intensive for someone with a disability. So if you are a friend or family member, be sure and ask what causes the most struggles and take it from there.

A quick word here about safety: the Apple Watch is phenomenal because it will call 911 if my arm hits the floor. If I tell the watch I'm okay, it does not dial for help. However, the watch gives me a minute to recover and then auto-dials if I don't move or respond. Some might think the Life Alert necklace around the neck does the same thing, but remember that if you pass out, you can't press the button. The Apple Watch solves that problem by acting "on its own."

Getting Dressed

Dressing can be a real chore for someone with CMT, especially when it comes to buttons. They are definitely a challenge I've overcome with a "button helper"—a device I hook through a buttonhole which allows me to grab the button and pull it through. Getting dressed is such a personal task, and I'm fortunate when Frank is home and can help with adjusting garments. He puts my earrings on for me, the earrings that need backs on them I can no longer do. If they just hook through the ear, then I am fine with doing those.

Due to my balance issues, Frank helps me finish pulling my pants up if I am having a hard time. Sometimes just gripping the waist, for example, with jeggings, can be hard. Some of my compression-type socks, which are softball socks, come up way over my knees so I can fold them over my braces, and they won't fall. He helps me put them on as well, but sometimes Frank even has a hard time with these since they are so tight. I don't understand why they make things like socks so hard to put on. Someone should make certain socks that are just for the disabled that wear braces. You would think someone would have figured this out and created some that aren't so difficult to put on. I don't know about other people, but I get so frustrated sometimes when I have to wear them.

More Personal Care

Speaking of personal tasks, something as simple as showering is definitely right up there with the more dangerous escapades. Many people with disabilities have mastered the art of "one-handed" head scrubbing, holding onto the rail and shampooing with a free hand, or better yet, using a shower chair makes hair washing so much easier. It's actually a wonderful treat when I have my hair cut and styled at a salon, for that's one less hair washing session that I have to handle myself. It's also not unusual for friends and family to shampoo their disabled loved one's hair in the sink and blow it dry—how helpful! Keep in mind that these kindnesses mean the world to people who struggle to do it by themselves.

Having sturdy handrails and a non-slip surface on the shower floor is vital. For instance, we installed an authentic handicap shower in my house, which has done light-years of good because I don't have to worry about getting in and out. It was a huge expense, but one of the better things I invested in.

But when you don't have the option to change out the shower, you may be operating with rails that slide down or pop off. The rubber begins to degrade over time, and someone needs to design better accessories. When he went out on his own, Ryan used suction cup-types of rails that came loose constantly. He was in an apartment, and that was all he could use.

Here's another task that requires a lot of organization—medicine, whether prescribed or over the counter. I have to mention pain creams or patches. If I need to manage my pain through this method, I really need someone else to place or rub it on my back. Honestly, I have a lot of pills to keep up with as well, and it's wonderful to have Frank around to help keep it all straight if I can't, or at least cut the pills in half, which is difficult for me to do. Both he and my mom have the list of all my medications. My "medicine regimen" may not work for everyone, but so far, the doctors have prescribed the following.

I took Cymbalta long ago when it first came out, an antidepressant as well as a nerve pain killer, but I don't find that it helps with nerve pain. I went back on it when Ryan died. I take Gabapentin in the evenings to help me sleep and alleviate the nerve pain in my legs and back. I take Nabumetone in the morning and evenings to help with the inflammation throughout my body (it's the strongest anti-inflammatory you can use). Tizanidine or Orphenadrine comes in handy when I'm having muscle spasms—it literally feels like my muscles start jumping and is not a good sensation. Klonopin is the medication I take the most to help control my tremors. Tylenol with codeine helps when the pain is really bad, but I don't sleep well when I take it. Everyone is affected differently by medications. Most of the time, doctors tell me that the side effects won't happen, and I always say they probably will or the total opposite will happen. My body is very sensitive to most medications, so I always take them with caution. Doctors do not always want to believe me until I call their office after taking them and had a strange reaction. I was actually told once, "Then there is nothing else I can do for you." I could not believe a doctor would say something like that so matter of fact. Isn't that what they are there for—to help figure out a treatment plan? They shouldn't just give up on patients!

As for over-the-counter medication, I take calcium to protect my bones due to falls. I also take flaxseed oil for heart health and daily vitamins for general health and make sure to have food coating my stomach throughout all this medicine ingestion.

I'm hoping that the neurological clinic will let me know if I'm taking the right medications. You heard that right—I'm not entirely convinced that I've been prescribed the correct type of pills and dosages. It's a smorgasbord of medicine that I'd like to be rid of, but in the meantime, depend upon. Educating family and friends about my daily rounds of prescriptions is important, so they are aware of my needs and can remind me, if needed, to coat my stomach with some sort of food, perhaps toast or crackers, to avoid damage to the lining of my stomach. I keep Frank and my mom updated in case I need to go to the hospital unconscious—they know what I'm on and can advise the emergency staff.

Meals

I remember when Ryan began having difficulties getting food to his mouth. I coached him on how to explain it when the kids at school asked questions. He simply told them it was part of his disease, and they seemed to accept that explanation. He didn't want to start on Klonopin, which would have helped with his tremors. At home, he used special utensils that were "fatter" in the grip and heavier, which helped steady his hands. By the way, I now get help with cutting up my meat or difficult foods if Frank is home. It's greatly appreciated, but sometimes I feel like such a little kid again. If Frank is not home, I do my best by myself.

I love to cook but find myself using the microwave oven more than ever. Actual cooking is certainly more difficult now, even for simple meals like spaghetti. My kitchen layout isn't the best because my stove and sink are too far apart to easily drain the pasta. This never was a problem until recently. So appropriate kitchen appliance layout is huge. Think about accessibility in your home, including cabinet height. If you are fortunate enough to be able to design your home, do so with the disability in mind so that you can accomplish a lot moving from point A to point B.

This brings me to the topic of a caregiver, someone who assists with day-to-day tasks like cooking. My mother actually has a cook who handles meals so that she can devote all her time to my dad's needs. There are also delivery service options depending on what area in which you live—Hello Fresh, Blue Apron, Home Chef, Green Chef, Sun Basket, Marley Spoon, Fresh and Easy, Diet To Go, Every Plate and many more. Of course, these options can be somewhat expensive. Thankfully, some grocery stores now offer curbside pick-up, which requires ordering online and then driving to pick up the order. This saves consumers from having to physically walk into the store.

Mobility

Although I am still able to walk, it's an awkward gait. I am dependent on my braces to keep me from falling so frequently. I might use a cane or walker, or just hang onto Frank's arm to keep me steady and upright.

But the truth is, I am falling more than ever. Getting off the floor is extremely difficult, especially if I bump my head or hurt a bone or joint. It's nice to walk next to someone who can help catch me in the act of stumbling and help me right myself. Carrying things while I'm walking is also a monumental challenge, and again, it's nice when someone carries packages or laundry for me. When I am alone, though, I don't always have my braces on, so I use my walker. At age forty-eight, I never thought I would be using a walker. Just like I never thought I'd be using a wheelchair, but if it keeps me from falling, I'm all for it.

Personally, there are still many things that I would love to participate in, but have to build up more strength to do them. For example, I'd like to scuba dive, but getting in and out of the water with all of the equipment would be difficult for me. I had a hard enough time snorkeling, but I would not have missed it for the world! I want to do more traveling, especially cruising to different places, but that is getting harder. Walking on the ship when I already have a balance problem is not easy, but at least I can take my scooter. I must keep someone with me often, but I do find ways around what might stand in my way.

I now have a scooter that comes apart in four pieces, so I don't need a lift on the back of a vehicle. That is great for me because if I want to go with someone else on a trip or a cruise, the scooter can be disassembled to fit in the vehicle or room. Flying is becoming less appealing because of all the charges for extra baggage, so unless I have to fly, I won't, with the exception of Australia. I will just have to be in my vehicle to see the rest of the places I want to go. Everything seems to have an extra challenge for me, but I'm not going to let that stop me from enjoying life as much as possible. I want to live life, not sit in fear of it, and that includes sharing all ventures with my dear husband.

Defenders

It's quite wonderful when you have a friend or significant other who thinks you are great just the way you are and sticks up for you in social situations. Frank is a very situationally-aware person. When people's eyes are staring at my legs, or I become a topic of conversation as we go out and about, he's likely to say, "Would you mind your own business?" I appreciate it. It feels good to have a defender. It feels good to have friends who watch out for me. It is sad that people would rather stare than ask me why I wore the braces or walked strangely.

My very best advice for those of you with a disabled friend or loved one is to let the world know that you admire and accept them and are proud to be seen with them. This bit of normality means the world to me, and I'm sure many others who enjoy "fitting in," if only for a momentary outing.

Employers

You have rights in the workplace, and the link https://www.eeoc.gov/eeoc/publications/fs-ada.cfm is a great source of information. According to the EEOC:

> *Title I of the Americans with Disabilities Act of 1990 prohibits private employers, state and local governments, employment agencies and labor unions from discriminating against qualified individuals with disabilities in job application procedures, hiring, firing, advancement, compensation, job training, and other terms, conditions, and privileges of employment.*
>
> *The ADA covers employers with 15 or more employees, including state and local governments. It also applies to employment agencies and to labor organizations. The ADA's nondiscrimination standards also apply to federal sector employees under section 501 of the Rehabilitation Act, as amended, and its implementing rules.*

You may not be aware that under the Americans with Disabilities Act (ADA), a "qualified employee or applicant with a disability is an individual who, with or without reasonable accommodation, can perform the essential functions of the job in question. Reasonable accommodation may include, but is not limited to:

- Making existing facilities used by employees readily accessible to and usable by persons with disabilities
- Job restructuring, modifying work schedules, reassignment to a vacant position
- Acquiring or modifying equipment or devices, adjusting or modifying examinations, training materials, or policies, and providing qualified readers or interpreters

This part is extremely important: "An employer generally does not have to provide a reasonable accommodation unless an individual with a disability has asked for one." In other words, you should ask for whatever you need to fulfill your duties. I call this "overcoming employment barriers, first by disclosing your disability and then by working around it."

An employer is required to make a "reasonable accommodation to the known disability of a qualified applicant or employee if it would not impose an 'undue hardship' on the operation of the employer's business. Reasonable accommodations are adjustments or modifications provided by an employer to enable people with disabilities to enjoy equal employment opportunities. Accommodations vary depending upon the needs of the individual applicant or employee. Not all people with disabilities (or even all people with the same disability) will require the same accommodation."

More on ADA Standards

I happen to work for a business that is not ADA compliant in several areas. I have fallen because the strip between the seams on the office floor was not completely glued down. There are slippery areas that are not made safe for me, an inaccessible bathroom with only a towel rack next to the toilet to help me down and up, and gravel walkways that can cause customers and the public to stumble. My employer does accommodate me with a wooden walkway leading to the door that I enter, but it can be very slippery when it rains; even though they did add a nonslip coating, it is still slippery. The ramp is starting to fall through, but they are fixing it. That is now the only entry since all the Covid-19 practices have started. We are considered an essential business, so we have stayed open the entire time, with the exception of a couple of weeks. Things wear down, but it takes forever to get them fixed. This makes it very daunting to never know if things are safe to get into my place of work or for other employees as well as customers.

As an employee, I deserve to be accommodated in commonsense ways, and so does the public. Buildings should be accessible to everyone. A good government site, the United States Access Board, offers a very good explanation at https://www.access-board.gov/guidelines-and-standards/buildings-and-sites/about-the-ada-standards.

> *Among other things, the Americans with Disabilities Act (ADA) ensures access to the built environment for people with disabilities. The ADA Standards establish design requirements for the construction and alteration of facilities subject to the law. These enforceable standards apply to places of public accommodation, commercial facilities, and state and local government facilities.*

No, building compliance cannot be ignored or "grandfathered in"—all buildings must be compliant. Check the "Other" link on the site to learn more about air travel, buildings and facilities, employment, housing, information and communication technology, programs and services, transportation, and voting.

One great CMT-related site, https://askjan.org/disabilities/Charcot-Marie-Tooth.cfm, give great disability rights information for those of us with CMT. For instance, if you have any questions or doubts about CMT being considered a disability, the site explains "medically qualifying" under a disability listing. It provides insights into qualifying for Social Security Disability as well.

Simple Pleasures

If you know someone with CMT and wish to treat them to something special, I suggest massages, chiropractic care, heating pads, and blankets. These thoughtful items are better than chocolate and roses, for sure. I am dependent on these necessities and enjoy them very much. Knots that form in my neck and shoulders have to be worked out of my body somehow, or I'd be so tight that moving around would be much more difficult. Massages are my favorite and help the tension in my whole body. In every state or city that I moved to after college, I found a masseuse.

The same goes for a chiropractor. Some people think that the "popping" noise at a chiropractor practice is horrible, but after a fall, it is precisely what I need and keeps my whole body in alignment. Now my masseuse works with my chiropractor by telling me what she might feel is out of place. She loosens things up really well and warms the muscles, so I can go and have a better adjustment the next day.

Heating pads and ice packs come next on the list of favorite items to have around the house since some areas of my body always seem to be swollen. When horse-riding was a constant in my life, it exacerbated the swelling, and I had to ice down after training.

So, if you are ever stumped at buying someone with CMT a gift, consider these suggestions—they will be much appreciated!

Intimacy

For some, the topic of sex and disabilities might be uncomfortable. However, it is an important topic and deserves our attention. I would like to recommend a scholarly article titled "Sexual functioning in women with mild and severe symptoms of Charcot-Marie-Tooth disease" by P. Gargiulo, P. Vinci, F. Navarro-Cremades and A. H. Rellini, published on the US National Library of Medicine, National Institutes of Health website (https://www.ncbi.nlm.nih.gov/pubmed/23534937). I've excerpted it below, and it confirms my personal experience of having a healthy, intimate marriage:

> *While conventional wisdom might predict that women with more severe complications have decreased sexual functioning and partner satisfaction relative to women with less severe presenting problems, the data did not support this assumption. In reality, symptom severity was positively associated with greater sexual functioning, despite those women reporting greater pain during intercourse. Moreover, such women were better satisfied with their partners in the capacity of a romantic relationship and felt sexually attractive to them. In both divisions of the MFSQ instrument [the McCoy Female Sexuality Questionnaire], however, trends in the CMT sample did not follow those of a normative group of women in an earlier study; whereas sexual functioning for healthy women decreased notably during middle adulthood (i.e., ages 41-50), women with CMT reported increasing functionality. A similar pattern was observed on the partner division of the MSFQ inventory, but increased capacities of the CMT sample were most apparent during younger adulthood (i.e., ages 31-40) and older adulthood (i.e., ages 51-60), respectively. To account for these observations, the authors asserted that, while scores of CMT women on the MSFQ were typically lower than that of the general population, functionality tended to approach levels comparable to the general population with age.*

Without getting too personal, medicines can affect intimacy levels because they cause dryness. Lubrication is a way around it. Pain, too, can be a barrier to intimacy either accommodated by medicine or by simply waiting for a less painful interlude. Long story short, I speak from experience when stating that women with CMT are just like females in general when it comes to sex and intimacy. I'll be honest—I'm not sure what the statistics are regarding males with CMT, but that should be fairly easy to research online.

Breathing

I would never have thought that breathing or trying to catch my breath would be an issue. Now that I am forty-eight years old with a neuromuscular disease, it turns out that as my disease progresses, it can be a big problem. I asked my neurologist first because it was very disheartening with all the

Covid-19 disease going around. I had been tested but was negative. I asked my neurologist if it could be related to my disease and was told that it would be rare. He told the nurse to tell me to see a pulmonologist. Since anything related to CMT is rare, I thought I deserved a better answer. I kept looking for a better explanation for my breathing problem while making an appointment with a pulmonologist like the neurologist suggested. When I called, the office couldn't get me in for a few weeks. Well great! I still could not catch my breath and sometimes found myself gasping for air to get enough oxygen. Before I even went to the pulmonologist, I ended up in the ER.

I'm alone during the week, and this happened on a Friday, so I knew my husband would be back from his trucking assignment at some point. My brother took me to the emergency room, and once they took me back in a room, he left since Frank was on his way. They took a CAT scan and ran a whole series of blood tests, and then gave me a breathing treatment. After all of that, the ER doctor came in and told me that all my tests looked good. He wasn't that familiar with CMT and told me to keep my pulmonologist appointment, and he would be able to look into it further. I just wanted to know why this was happening. I was put on a waiting list for the pulmonologist doctor in case someone canceled, so I could get in sooner. Unfortunately, that never happened.

The following are good articles that describe respiratory problems in a CMT patient.

- https://www.hnf-cure.org/living-with-cmt/breathing-problems
- https://charcot-marie-toothnews.com/charcot-marie-tooth-and-the-Lungs

I finally made it to the pulmonologist, and he started me on Ipratropium Bromide Solution, which was put into my breathing machine for the first five days. It seemed to help for the first four to five hours, and then I did another round from 4-4:30. I was supposed to do three a day, but it dried out my mouth and nose so badly that the doctor switched to twice a day. Then I was put on an Incruse Ellipta inhaler for the next five days. This was the first step to see if it would help me breathe easier. At the time of this writing, I'm on the second day of the inhaler, which seems to be doing better than the breathing treatments. The doctor also ordered a breathing test and an echocardiogram at the hospital. I did have the tests done, and my breathing test came out fine. The doctors are now trying to figure out what might be wrong with my heart. I have been to a cardiologist, and he did not hear anything wrong with my heart. He even put me through a chemical stress test, which is what you have to do when you can't run on a treadmill. The second half of the test was excruciatingly painful, and for a few minutes, it felt as if my chest was being ripped open. My heart was racing so extremely fast that I thought I might have a heart attack. The person running the test assured me that my heart was doing fine since he was monitoring it on the screen and said the pain would stop in just a minute. My heart finally calmed down, and after two hours and thirty minutes of that test, the doctor said my heart was strong. I told him that it should be since I survived that. At this point, the cardiologist didn't know what was wrong with my breathing. I just wish more doctors knew what to do for CMT patients with respiratory issues.

My next appointment was with an internist. Her specialty was internal medicine, but she also performed regular doctor care. The best thing about her was she had studied CMT! Finally, a doctor that might be able to help. As I write this, she is consulting with all of the other doctors I've seen, getting test results and has scheduled me to have a Barium Swallowing test and a heart cath. The swallowing test is to make sure that nothing is malfunctioning since I told her I have choking problems occasionally. After looking at my echocardiogram, she thinks that the blood in the right ventricle of my heart is flowing backward, causing my breathing problems, and that is why she wants a heart cath done. This will let her see how my heart is functioning.

CHAPTER 16
GIVING BACK

To know even one life has breathed easier because you have lived. This is to have succeeded.
~ Ralph Waldo Emerson

I recently signed up to be a CMT advocate, joining others to ensure that our collective voice is heard on public policy issues that are important to the community. By becoming involved, I hope to make a difference today and in the future. There are often opportunities to speak in schools and on university campuses about inclusion, diversity, and health challenges. I mentioned previously that "sensitivity training" lacked when I was a student, but today's atmosphere is more inclusionary, thank heavens.

At times, schools set aside time to hear from guest speakers. Sometimes they might pair adults with disabilities with groups of children with special needs. There is a demand for speakers who can connect with those with disabilities, spreading the message of acceptance and inclusion, but also demonstrating that people with disabilities share a lot in common with others without disabilities. People are people, regardless of their journey through life.

Consider volunteering at your local schools. Contact the administration and let them know you are willing. It will help today's children embrace the value of all human beings and mold them into people with a social conscience. It will lessen the bullying and increase acceptance. Imagine a world filled with compassionate people—it begins with us and our willingness to step out of our comfort zones.

We can only move forward when people lend their voices and share their journeys. I personally feel this is the ultimate way of giving back, especially in elementary, junior high and high school classrooms. We can give back by helping prepare kids for the reality of living amidst a variety of people, each with their own abilities and value.

Outreach

I mentioned at the start of the book that people with CMT certainly can serve others through their jobs and by volunteering and participating in outreach. Our vision is a world without CMT, and to help get there, we can do something as simple as attending CMT events. The "Charcot-Marie-Tooth Association: The Time is Now" Facebook page has a calendar full of these get-togethers so others can meet, support one another and get involved.

For instance, the CMTA held a Patient/Family Conference at the Le Méridien Atlanta Perimeter Hotel in November with a light breakfast and a lunch with CMT experts on topics such as neurology, genetics, surgery, research updates, physical therapy and more. Renowned CMT neurologist Dr. Michael Shy, foot and ankle surgeon Dr. Glenn Pfeffer, pulmonologist Dr. Ashraf Elsayegh, CMTA Board Chair Gilles Bouchard and gene therapy expert Dr. Scott Harper were guest speakers, as well as CMTA CEO Amy Gray and medical professionals in the areas of physical therapy, orthotics, genetic counseling, and more.

CMT Events were recently held in Anchorage, Buffalo, Chicago, Cleveland, Denver, Fort Worth, Las Vegas, Long Island, Milwaukee, Minneapolis, Pittsburg, Sarasota, Seattle and Tulsa—just to name a few in the United States! I noticed that events were held outside the U.S., such as in Canada. Much of the focus of these gatherings was how patients could be partners in the research process. I believe that is the bottom line—we should all be partners in research, and so much of this has to do with fundraising.

Moving for Better Health

Let's face it. I have a normal life expectancy while dealing with a progressive disease and would like as "normal" a life as possible. I ride an exercise bike, and CMTA also recommends swimming and exercises you can do at home, for example, yoga, pilates and tai chi. They feature an "Exercise and Physical Therapy for Inherited Neuropathies" section on their website with a video series for balance, endurance, flexibility, strength, and more. You can participate at your own level of comfort and watch it with a partner who will then better understand your abilities and limitations. Check it out!

We can't deny the crucial role fitness plays in slowing the progression of CMT symptoms. The story of Hereditary Neuropathy Founder (HNF) Allison Moore is nothing short of amazing. She was unable to finish the 1995 NYC Marathon due to a cancer diagnosis and the severe onset of CMT from the chemotherapy. Twenty-three years later, she walked the 2018 NYC Marathon. I find that inspirational!

These exercise-types of events remain an effective way to share knowledge and raise funds, and inspired the creation of Team CMT in 2007 by founder Chris Wodke, who has CMT. Team CMT is a grassroots community fundraising program through the HNF, and focuses on exercise and awareness. It has 213 members in 39 states and 12 countries. Participation is easy, and so is donating—just click the donation buttons on their website. Team CMT events are easily shared on social media, as well, and sharing online is an effortless way of supporting good causes.

Here's another motivational story. In 2012, Chris received her acceptance letter to run in the 2012 Boston Marathon Mobility Impaired Division. She is a fierce advocate in promoting exercise for people with CMT and enrolling others in Team CMT. I like her reminder to increase awareness by having team members wear a Team CMT singlet or t-shirt wherever they exercise, such as the gym, walking in a park or at events. This made me realize that I should wear CMT-related apparel any time I can. It's just an effortless way to bring awareness and start conversations.

As of the printing of this memoir, HNF has raised over $256,000 for CMT research and is now recognized as a leading program to encourage patients to be active, while at the same time support HNF's mission to increase awareness of CMT and raise funds for research.

The CMT Community event, HNF's Movement is Medicine™ Summit in Phoenix, AZ, November 13-14, 2020, advocates for physical activity as an essential role in physical and mental well being, especially for people affected by debilitating diseases like CMT. The Movement is Medicine™ mission is to promote the safe adoption of a more active lifestyle through exercise and nutrition programs specifically created for those with disabilities and can be found on the hnf-cure.org website.

Walking for the Cure

Another outreach involves walks for the cure. You can check out the CMT Exercise Video Series on the CMTA website for mobility inspiration and ideas. It states: "The American Medical Association, the American College of Sports Medicine, the United States Department of Health and Human Services, and the Office of the United States Surgeon General, all agree that children and adults with chronic disease and disability, who are capable, should engage in regular forms of activity and exercise."

The wonderful thing is, events that include CMT walks and bike rides help us stay in shape while promoting our message of inclusion and awareness. Better yet, it can help raise much-needed funds for our cause. But check with your doctor before exercising, even for a good local cause, because it's part of our own due diligence to ensure we are up to the challenge and can participate safely.

As a child, I participated in MDA walks. People pledged a nickel, dime or quarter per mile that I walked, and I went as far as I could. When I couldn't take another step, I was loaded into the "poop out" van with others who could not quite finish the walk. I remember getting full credit for the pledges because I only had a quarter mile or so left to finish.

Today, CMT walks are well attended throughout the country as volunteer-led national fundraising campaigns for the Charcot-Marie-Tooth Association. By participating in these year-round campaigns, we join hundreds of others nationwide in giving back. It may seem like a small way to improve the lives of those living with CMT, but when we Walk 4 CMT, we help fund patient programs and treatment research initiatives to better the lives of the 2.8 million people living with CMT. The funds raised by Walk 4 CMT improve quality of life with the goal of one day finding the elusive cure.

Families, friends and corporate supporters show up to walk for CMT, sometimes in wheelchairs, and it does my heart good to see children involved as well. They often form teams and enjoy the social aspects of sharing their CMT journeys. Most importantly, they forge friendships and band together—a real-life "power in numbers" movement. I like that the "Why Walk for CMT" section on the site gives testimonials from parents and kids about their diagnosis and unique outlooks. The events offer music, refreshments, t-shirts and fun activities in addition to the actual walks. I also like that the site shows the dollar amounts raised around the nation, such as the Washington D.C. Walk 4 CMT that raised $40,960.61, the Denver Walk for CMT that raised $27,227.60, the Palo Alto Walk for CMT that raised $22,687.20, the Atlanta Walk 4 CMT that raised $15,263.20 and the Parkland Walk 3 CMT that raised $14,656.70.

Collectively, these five events raised more than six figures for research, spread community awareness, and provided a fun outing for the participants. Anytime we can bring attention to rare diseases like CMT, we make a difference.

Biking for the Cause

People can ride bicycles to support the Charcot-Marie-Tooth Association as well. The organization cycle4cmt.com has set up links so that participants can create and register their "OWN" Rider Program. Now anyone, anywhere, can be involved, take fun pictures and post their adventures on the Cycle4CMT Facebook page. I recommend getting familiar with the CMTA website, for it shares so much information. I enjoyed an article about riding bicycles—great for those of us with CMT because it is non-impact, doesn't stress joints, and we don't trip while bike riding. It's another exercise option in addition to walking, wheeling and swimming.

The article recommends a few tips such as getting a professional bike fit "from someone with a lot of experience" and to give yourself time to get used to the bike and various roads and trails. Oh—and wear a helmet! They weigh only a few ounces and are well enough ventilated that even on a summer day, they provide shade and keep you cooler than wearing no helmet. Also, the article recommends that we use clipless pedals and shoes, set the release tension nice and tight to help our weak and unstable ankles without worrying about our feet coming off the pedal. It's amazing what you can find online. I found a forum for those who cycle with CMT and other exercise-related groups. The internet is our friend and allows information to be just one "Google" away. It unites us as we seek to advocate.

The Dog Shelter

"Giving back" isn't exclusive to CMT outreach. My personal way of giving back has included volunteering at my local animal shelter. I need to be around positive souls, and people who step up for animals are my kind of people.

As hard as the volunteers try, the shelter needs help. They have a lot of work ahead of them to improve the kennels and their level of animal care. Many small shelters face a David vs. Goliath type of situation where so much rides on donations, funding and people who are willing to give their time.

Please consider volunteering at your local shelter in any capacity, including financial donations. Every bit counts. It is meaningful work, and they need us. I just work in the office right now and am not sure I'll be able to do any sort of hands-on work with the dogs and puppies. It remains to be seen if I can adjust to my Dynamic Braces and keep my balance without falling when a dog leaps up on me. But my presence at the shelter helps—maybe in a small way, and that's the point. If we can all play some small part, then collectively, we are a part of a larger solution.

There is no reason why people with CMT can't contribute to the greater good. If we think about it and look for opportunities, we can shine as volunteers.

CMT Service Dogs

This brings me to the topic of service dogs who are trained to help those of us with CMT. I know that not just any dog can adapt to being a service companion for people with my disease. In fact, inspire.com hosted a webinar in August 2019 titled "CMT & Canine Companions Online Webinar - Charcot-Marie-Tooth (CMT)."

I checked into adopting a service dog, but there are such long waiting lists and numerous rules, not to mention all of the paperwork, photos of my house, and a two-week training course for the dog and me. Frank would have to attend as well since I would be required to bring along the person who is with me in the house the most. That equals two missed weeks of work for us both, so I kind of put that on the back burner.

My hope has always been to find the right dog at the Nacogdoches Animal Shelter with the appropriate temperament and ability to accept the training. I have prayed every night for a dog who is willing to please, doesn't chew furniture, is house trained, is loyal, and who can endure the rigors of learning what it means to assist someone with CMT. My dog Mandy comes to mind; may she rest in peace. She was part Collie and part Labrador, and came into our lives when my barn dog Domino was still alive, and it took a while for them to warm up to each other. Mandy did agility training and shows when Ryan was growing up. She was just so smart and receptive to commands, and there just aren't many dogs in the world like her or Domino. So I had to remind myself of that fact and not set my expectations extraordinarily high.

I was temporarily fostering a golden retriever mix, which I thought might be a good candidate. However, she jumped on Frank and knocked him down before going to work. He then didn't trust her with me. He sent me a text, so I would be careful with her that morning. I certainly was careful and had no issues that first day.

But sure enough, she did more harm than good when I fell one night. She simply didn't know what to do and was all over me. Of course, none of this was her fault at all; she's a very sweet dog and successfully found a home with a different owner. But it became painfully obvious that I needed a dog with a quieter disposition, old enough to have outgrown the antics and exuberance of puppyhood, but young enough to be trainable. Also, I needed a dog who would know instinctively that I have vulnerabilities and could respond accordingly.

And Then Came Dixie

Thankfully, we found Dixie at the Longview Rescue—a standard dachshund mixed with a bit of Chihuahua. She knows when to "kennel up" most of the time and does it much better with treat incentives. We are also working on "stay" and any obedience commands, so she listens to me. She does this best when I'm alone with her. Dixie is really attached to Frank and listens to him so much more quickly. He jokingly says it is probably because Dixie sees him as the alpha male.

Is she the right size to be a full-blown CMT service dog? Not really. There is no way she can support my body or help when I fall. However, she is just the right size to be a comfort and companion animal—I can hold her in my lap—and she's such a good girl. Funny too! She caught her reflection in the glass of our TV/media stand and just barked and barked at herself. It made us laugh. Now she actually watches the TV from the couch and runs to the TV when something exciting is on the screen. If a cat commercial comes on, she barks. If a dog commercial comes on, she whines and begs for the dog to come and play. When an animal show from Animal Planet comes on, it gets quite noisy! We'll see if she can stand still when I fall without "getting in the way" when I try to pick myself up. Recently, I experienced that she runs around me and wants to make sure that I'm okay when I fall. Any loud noise she hears me make Dixie makes sure that I'm alright. So far, she's learned the words "move," "sit," "down," "shake," "high five," and "get him."

Dixie always has the one "radar" ear up.

As someone with CMT who owns a dog, particularly because I have an advanced form of CMT, I do want to exercise sensibly when I can, and without excuses. So now I have Dixie as a sidekick—she'll run around me or across my abs when I do sit-ups. Or, she'll shove a toy at me. I can take her out on rugged walks on my scooter on uneven terrain. She isn't judgmental and just loves to be in the moment. Her little legs keep up with my scooter.

I even found the "GoGo Stik, The Totally Clean Pooper Scooper" online, something I might buy to use on our walks because bending over to pick up her droppings just isn't an option. I think I could use the GoGo Stik without too many complications.

Long story short, we dote on Dixie like she was our child. She has added a dimension of fun, bonding and adoration as dogs tend to do. We are blessed to be adoptive "pet parents" to a dog in need. I suspect we needed Dixie as much as she needed us!

Ryan's Contributions

Ryan often said he hated school… that is, until he enrolled in college. He really blossomed in the honor society for his IT group and belonged to a business fraternity that I think had something to do with computers. He contributed volunteer hours at a computer place (like an internship) and fixed whatever they assigned him.

He graduated with honors, and I was so proud that Ryan followed this calling and pursued a wonderful career. He headed into an industry that he loved, equipped to carve out a life for himself. Before his death, he lived independently and made the most of his full-time job and his side business, Schaeffer IT. His last professional social media post was:

Let's finish the holidays strong. Fix a loved one's computer today for 20% off any COMPUTER REPAIR done between now and December 31. Merry Christmas to all, stay safe out there this holiday season!!

His permanent social marketing lingo and call-to-action stated:

You might be wondering why your computer is running slow or if you really need all of those photo albums. Schaeffer IT can help with all of IT!! We have services that range from computer repair to consultation to photography editing. We are dedicated to serving the customer. Whatever your IT need is, we hope we can provide a service that can fulfill that need. Forget having to pay high-end cost for IT services—just come to Schaeffer IT, and we guarantee we will be the lowest.

All IT services are done onsite so you can sit in the comfort of your home while we take care of all your IT needs, no matter how big or small. All you have to do to get started is to call or click the Learn More button above to get forwarded to our site, or you can just send us a message.

Ryan was fiercely independent. It was just breathtaking to watch him grow into adulthood. I admit to biting my nails a few times as he ventured out on his own. His first apartment smelled like cigarettes, and Ryan was allergic. He moved into his second apartment with his same roommate during the last year of school, and it was simply godawful. He was working at ABC auto at the time. When I visited him in 2017, he had no air conditioning, heat, washer or dryer… but plenty of water! The apartment leaked water everywhere, even out of the outlets! It was an extremely unsafe residence. The water damage in the living room and bedroom was extensive and ruined his desk; all of the rooms were wet. Ryan even had to suck up water in the hallway.

My concerns were that he'd be too cold in the winter and get sick, or catch an illness from the mold, or get electrocuted when plugging something into a sopping wet outlet. The landlord wouldn't do anything about it. Ryan went to a lawyer to see what he could do to get the landlord to play nice.

The lawyer said there wasn't enough to go on to pursue money damages, but he offered to do a demand letter. Finally, his dad offered to move him to an RV park and let Ryan use his RV. Ryan did end up in an RV park close to Longview, which was better than living with water everywhere. Ryan absolutely did love his father, but we could hear him yelling at his father through the phone. Yes, maintaining independent relationships was part of "adulting," and Ryan was forging his own bonds and boundaries with his loved ones.

And then he grew angel wings. I cannot begin to fathom God's plan in all of this, other than to revel in the blessing my son gave to the world. So many people commented on his sense of humor, but also his compassion. He was a good friend, one that didn't judge. I think one of his unique ways of "giving back" had to do with his ability to listen and sympathize with his friends, no matter what they happened to be going through. He understood them on the deepest level because he had faced and overcome so many of his own challenges.

CHAPTER 17
RESEARCH

No research is ever quite complete. It is the glory of a good bit of work that it opens the way for something still better, and this repeatedly leads to its own eclipse.
~ Mervin Gordon

Right now, CMT is considered incurable, but that was said of other diseases throughout the centuries that were eradicated, such as smallpox and rinderpest. Polio is on the verge of being eradicated, and great strides have been made regarding malaria. There is hope for a cure for CMT as well through science and medical studies. Even if a cure is never found, advancements in treatments and surgeries will continue to be uncovered. Each step toward improvement is a step in the right direction in this ever-changing realm of research.

Don't blink—who knows what new discoveries will be made in the future. Right now, the particular progress and studies below have jumped out at me as something worthy to share. I wasn't aware of all of this progress until I began developing this chapter, so I hope the experimentation and breakthroughs will be interesting to you as well.

Timeline of Progress

We would all like to live in a world without CMT, and I am grateful for studies that can help us understand it, treat it, and deal with the disease until a breakthrough occurs, and it becomes curable. This is why it is so important that medical and scientific research continues. It's so interesting to learn about the timeline of research progress within the CMT community from the Charcot Marie Tooth Association (CMTA):

- In 1995, the CMTA began awarding fellowship grants to CMT

researchers.

- In 2001, a patient database was created for North America in conjunction with Wayne State University.
- The Strategy to Accelerate Research (STAR) program was created in 2008, thanks to generous contributions by two CMTA families.
- In 2010, the organization brought together globally recognized CMT specialists for a CMT Type 2 research symposium.
- In 2012, CMTA established 11 Centers of Excellence to help patients get the best possible evaluation and care.
- In 2014, the organization added CMTA types 1X, 1B, 2A, 2E, and 4 to its research platform.
- In 2018, in collaboration with the pharmaceutical company Ionis, the CMTA announced a major breakthrough in CMT1A gene-targeting research—the exact type of CMT that both Ryan and I shared.

Thirty-Five Years

Speaking of the year 2018, the CMTA celebrated its 35th anniversary with the $150,000 Research Challenge as a way to help reach its fundraising goal. Initially, CMTA was called the National Foundation for Peroneal Muscular Atrophy, a nonprofit established thirty-five years ago by a group of CMT families and physicians in New York. It grew into the organization we know today.

Donations in the 35th-anniversary fundraiser were matched dollar for dollar to benefit the STAR program and its scientific advisers. STAR now has five key elements: 1.) Assays, (tests), 2.) animal models, 3.) stem cells, 4.) partners, and 5.) clinical trials. Over the last two years, CMTA has increased its research partnerships with pharmaceutical, biotechnology and research service companies. Since its inception, the organization has steered $8 million to research.

In 2019, researchers worked on eighteen projects involving Charcot-Marie-Tooth. The chief goal now is accelerating into clinical trial breakthroughs in gene and broad-based therapies for all types of CMT for the three million people worldwide who suffer from it. Some quick references are below, and I find them gratifying and comforting.

- The CMTA has spent over $10M in recent years and expects to spend about $10M in the near future to help bring CMT drugs to market. We currently have over 44 active research projects with top labs around the world, all vetted through our medical STAR Advisory Board, which comprises 30 of the most pre-eminent CMT scientists from across the globe.

- The CMTA has a network of twenty-eight CMTA Centers of Excellence and a partnership with the Inherited Neuropathies Consortium (INC). Through this network, we are building patient registries and outcome measures for our pharmaceutical and biotech partners to aid in fast and effective clinical trials.
- The CMTA now has partnership agreements with more than twenty pharmaceutical, biotech and research service organizations across three continents.
- The CMTA are leaders in the latest genetic and neurological technologies (such as CRISPR, gene therapy, gene silencing, axon and muscle regeneration) and are actively working with the CMTA to develop treatments and a cure for people living with CMT.

You can follow CMTA online at www.cmtausa.org and read the most recent articles, such as Another $500,000 Pledge to Type 2 Research!; New Gene Therapy, Type 1/Type 4 Research Projects Approved; New Gene Therapy Development Program for CMT2A; $1 Million Gift Pledged to CMT Type 2 Research; The CMT&ME Study: What It's Like to Live with CMT; Patients as Partners Profiles; Type 1 CMT Gene Therapy Project Now Underway; and CMTA Announces $1 Million in Funding for STAR Research Projects.

Advances with CMT1A

The severity and progression of CMT depend on what type of mutation we have. That affects what treatments work for us. As I wrote this chapter, I was excited to see the research being done on my type of CMT (CMT1A) around the nation and overseas, which reminds me again that my disease is considered rare, but still affects people on every continent. I am definitely not alone on this journey.

Researchers are studying genes known to cause my disease and the way mutations affect these genes. They are also trying to identify additional genes that cause CMT and why. It has led researchers to the development of therapies that could prevent or treat the disease, still very preliminary. A number of research groups are focusing on increasing the understanding of CMT and developing ways to diagnose it, such as the TREAT-CMT project, a collaboration between twelve research groups in Spain to study additional mutations, discover biomarkers that can flag the disease, and developing cell or animal models of CMT that can be used to test treatments.

Pharnext developed PXT3003 to treat people with CMT type 1A. It works by blocking PMP22, a protein in some CMT1A patients who overproduce PMP22 and experience nerve damage. Phase 2 clinical trials showed PXT3003 to be a promising and safe treatment for CMT1A, as published in the Orphanet Journal of Rare Diseases. Phase 3 trial of the therapy will be an international, randomized, double-blind, placebo-controlled trial called PLEO-CMT. In addition, it is doing a long-term safety extension study of PXT3003 that it has dubbed PLEO-CMT-FU.

Another example of a CMT investigational drug is ACE-083, developed by Acceleron Pharma for improvement of strength and muscle mass. After positive results in Phase 1 clinical trials, Acceleron has started a Phase 2 trial. Regulators have approved a request by another company, Addex Therapeutics, to test its CMT1A drug ADX71441 in clinical trials. This is all very good news for those of us with CMT1A. I encourage you to look for clinical trials regarding your particular type of CMT.

Gene Therapy and Stem Cell Therapy

Below is an explanation of the differences between gene therapy and stem cell therapy:

1. Gene therapy involves delivering a functional copy of a gene that is faulty in the disease.
2. Stem cell therapy involves delivering healthy cells to promote nerve regeneration.

Researchers conduct studies in order to advance to the clinical trial stage. For instance, in a study of a CMT1A mouse model, researchers used a virus to deliver a functional version of the NT-3 gene. That gene is involved in the survival of Schwann Cells, which maintain the protective myelin sheath that surrounds the nerves. The delivery of a functional gene appeared to promote nerve regeneration.

I'd like to interject a word here about the use of animal research and testing. I wish animal testing, largely rodent-based, was not needed. I wish with all my heart that CMT research could be cruelty-free. Unfortunately, with science so complex that it involves gene and stem cell therapy, there appears to be no other way to work toward an understanding of how and why CMT exists.

A 2013 case study by Bouhy and Timmerman (American Neurological Association) titled "Animal models and therapeutic prospects for Charcot-Marie-Tooth disease" addresses the challenges:

The increasing number of genes linked to the disease, and their considerable clinical and genetic heterogeneity render the development of these strategies particularly challenging. In this context, cellular and animal models provide powerful tools. Efficient motor and sensory tests have been developed to assess the behavioral phenotype in transgenic animal models (rodent and fly). When these models reproduce a phenotype comparable to CMT, they allow therapeutic approaches and the discovery of modifiers and biomarkers. In this review, we describe the most convincing transgenic rodent and fly models of CMT and how they can lead to clinical trial. We also discuss the challenges that the research, the clinic, and the pharmaceutical industry will face in developing efficient and accessible treatment for CMT patients.

Genetic heterogeneity, by the way, is a rather complicated term. According to the cancer.gov NCI Dictionary of Genetics Terms, it is defined as the production of the same or similar phenotypes by different genetic mechanisms. There are two types: 1.) allelic heterogeneity – when different alleles at a locus can produce variable expression of a condition; and 2.) locus heterogeneity – the term used to describe disease in which mutations at different loci can produce the same disease phenotype. If you are anything like me, a curious and ardent internet researcher of medical terminology, you can further study genetic heterogeneity and other terms.

On a personal note, Frank went through gene therapy when he faced prostate, liver and colon cancer—he had a zero percent survival rate. Yet, he was cured and noted that the physicians removed his cancer cells from the affected areas and manipulated the cancer cells to turn them off. Then they re-inserted the manipulated cells and waited to see if it would work.

After a bit of time, it cured all of his cancer, and he is still cancer-free to this day! However, the place closed down after people began to be healed. Frank suspects it's because the pharmaceutical and chemotherapy industries did not want to lose money.

An Important Grant

For everyone interested in CMT research, in particular for CMT1A research, a "Progress Now" Research and Clinical Trial Update recently published news that Michael Shy, Ph.D., at the University of Iowa was awarded an MDA Clinical Research Network Grant of $423,413 to further develop the Inherited Neuropathies Consortium, a network of clinical investigators dedicated to creating the infrastructure needed to evaluate therapies for people with inherited peripheral neuropathies collectively known as CMT.

Briefly, in addition to expanding historical data to become "clinical-trial ready," the primary aim is to establish a large longitudinal cohort of patients whose data will be used to study disease progression, look for genetic modifiers to CMT1A, and identify new genetic causes for axonal forms of CMT.

Visit rarediseasesnetwork.org to learn more about this important research and ongoing progress.

National Institutes of Health

In the quest to find a cure, I'm hopeful that the efforts encompassing the globe right now are successful. Work is being done in areas where people have different cultures and life experiences, and it simply bonds the CMT community together. People are people, no matter where they are born, and it just so happens that many of us face a rare disease that crops up internationally.

Because it is a rare disease, CMT does not get the same attention and funding as diseases that affect larger populations of patients, such as breast cancer or Lou Gehrig's Disease (ALS). I certainly don't begrudge anyone the funding, but I wish all diseases were of "equal importance," including rare diseases, because every life is precious and everyone's health is crucial. Therefore, I support research that helps those of us with diseases that are lesser-known. Just because CMT is lesser-known does not make it of "lesser importance."

I encourage anyone with a disability to look up the various organizational, governmental and philanthropic agencies that exist to share information and conduct research, especially on behalf of us with CMT. The National Institutes of Health (NIH) is a great resource. At the time of this writing, several studies for Charcot Marie Tooth Disease are underway worldwide and being tracked by the NIH.

Many studies seek volunteer participants, mostly in larger cities with medical centers or research facilities. This makes it difficult for those of us with mobility issues and jobs to participate, for it is not always feasible to take off work or travel hours away from home. However, for some, there are nearby opportunities. It's just a matter of finding them.

The National Institutes of Health has listed recruitment opportunities for the following:

- Registered Cohort Study on Charcot-Marie-Tooth Disease in China
- Impact of Charcot-Marie-Tooth Disease in the Real World in the United Kingdom,
- Natural History Evaluation of Charcot Marie Tooth Disease (CMT) Types CMT1B, CMT2A, CMT4A, CMT4C, and Others in California

- Genetics of Charcot Marie Tooth (CMT) - Modifiers of CMT1A, New Causes of CMT2 in Connecticut
- Study of ACE-083 in Patients With Charcot-Marie-Tooth Disease in Colorado
- Natural History Study of Charcot-Marie-Tooth 4J (CMT4J)" in Texas
- Change in MUNIX in Patients With CMT1A Undergoing a Home Ankle Strengthening Program Versus Standard of Care in Tennessee
- And many more

Muscular Dystrophy Association

The Muscular Dystrophy Association (MDA) is a qualified 501(c)(3) tax-exempt organization and has a Science & Research link. I signed up for their newsletters and receive informative emails, and one recently landed in my inbox stating:

Dear friend,

We have some exciting news to share with you:

MDA announced the awarding of 25 new grants totaling more than $6.6 million toward research focused on a variety of rare neuromuscular diseases (NMDs), including amyotrophic lateral sclerosis, Charcot-Marie-Tooth disease, congenital muscular dystrophy, Duchenne muscular dystrophy, facioscapulohumeral muscular dystrophy, Friedreich's ataxia, inclusion body myositis, limb-girdle muscular dystrophy, mitochondrial myopathy, myotonic dystrophy, spinal-bulbar muscular atrophy, and spinal muscular atrophy.

This round of grant funding reinforces MDA's unwavering commitment to the progress of neuromuscular disease research and builds on the more than $1 billion MDA has already invested in research to uncover new treatments and cures for NMDs since its inception.

The newly funded projects will aim to advance research discoveries and new therapy development in multiple areas. The awarded grants will fund studies to further advance our understanding of the causes of NMDs, investigate new approaches to developing treatments and therapies, and improve how clinical trials are designed and implemented.

For more on this exciting news, read MDA Awards 25 Grants Totaling More Than $6.6 Million for Neuromuscular Disease Research for updates.

Sincerely,

MDA Outreach

Possible Link between CMT1A and MS

While I'm all for research, sometimes I hear news that causes concern. A report published in Charcot-Marie-ToothNews.com, August 2019, shared that PMP22 defects may be a link between CMT1A and multiple sclerosis. The case report study, "A special association between Charcot-Marie-Tooth type 1A disease and relapsing remitting multiple sclerosis," was published in Multiple Sclerosis and Related Disorders.

The case study states: "Our patient is one of the rare cases with CMT1A that developed a demyelinating illness fulfilling the diagnostic criteria for MS. The increasing number of cases with CMT and MS may point to the relationship between the two diseases, [possibly resulting from duplications on the PMP22 gene]," they stated. "PMP22, the target protein in CMT1A [and] a component of myelin, [is very similar] with other CNS proteins. [Therefore,] the PMP22 gene might be relevant to a common pathway of the demyelinating process."

The conclusion?

"Although the simultaneous existence of CMT1A and MS in our patient could be coincidental, we suggest that inherited peripheral demyelination may trigger an auto-immune reaction against CNS myelin."

My take from this report is that we should be talking to our doctors about this new research. We can't assume they already know—it's quite obvious to many CMT patients that we often have to educate our physicians.

TeleMedicine

Here's something fairly new. MDA also emailed me a newsletter describing the use of "telemedicine" in which people living with neuromuscular disease can access medical care online. Thanks to modern technology, some MDA Care Center locations are now able to use telemedicine to make sure that MDA families, regardless of where they live, can get the expert care they need when they need it.

Telemedicine is the remote delivery of care using audio and video conferencing and costs less for families while allowing doctors to adjust treatment plans, change medications or modify respiratory care quickly and easily.

This isn't available everywhere yet, but in a 16-month trial, doctors at the Massachusetts General Hospital had 136 televisits with 97 people living with ALS, a neuromuscular disease that leads to the widespread loss of muscle use. For these patients, the convenience and ease of talking to their doctors from their homes have been critical in prioritizing their care and comfort while minimizing the number of disruptions in their daily lives.

The newsletter explained that even smartphones could help doctors monitor individual health closely and measure individual patterns from a distance. Smartphones have sensors that can be activated to evaluate a person's ability to perform finger movements and cognitive tasks.

Donating to Science

Last but not least, I am an avid proponent of organ donations and have always felt compelled to donate my body to science. This is a very personal decision that became extremely important in light of Ryan's death, although I don't know all the specifics. Apparently, it requires giving consent to an anatomical institute and some advanced planning. I plan to talk to CMTA to see how I can do so, knowing that research on my body may help scientists and doctors better understand the disease and improve or even create new medical technologies. If CMTA does not facilitate body donations, I will donate elsewhere if possible—the internet is full of information on the topic.

CHAPTER 18
RESOURCES

The heart is nature's most immense untapped resource. Utilizing the power of the heart is the most significant choice you will make in life.
~ Steven Redhead, Keys to the Laws of Creation

We all want to manage CMT and find help, tips and advice. Every reader of this book has probably already identified resources that are disability-friendly, and my goal is to add to your potential resources with blogs, websites, books, magazines and videos that have inspired me every step of the way.

CMT Clinicians

Most of us struggle in finding healthcare and doctors who specialize in our disease. Perhaps this resource from CMTA will help. Check out the link www.cmtausa.org/resource-directory/wpbdp_category/cmt-clinicians/ to use the resource directory for CMT specialists in the United States. I searched by zip code and believe this directory lists worldwide clinicians as well.

Popular CMT Bloggers

I'd like to recommend several blogs that are CMT-oriented and affirming. Lainie Ishbia is a social worker, disability speaker, blogger and happy life curator with a following at trendable.com. She interviews interesting people with disabilities to showcase how we can live confident and happy lives.

Sarah Wells is a "CMT warrior" and mom who cares about the impact of CMT on her children. She shares interesting adventures and regular fresh ideas about chronic health, wellness and navigating the 'systems' at mystripylife.com.

Elizabeth M. Ouellette highlights the "ups and downs, the horizontals, the inside outs and the upside downs of living with CMT or Charcot-Marie-Tooth Disease" at bestfoot4wardblog.com. Neither she nor her husband has the disease, but her son does. She has devoted her life to "sharing the very real experiences of living with CMT, including CMT foot reconstruction surgery, perceived differences, teaching kids about CMT, CMT awareness... you get it—all things CMT!"

Ashley Pomykala of Parsimonious Pash is a mom, disabled student, part-time worker and avid couponer "living with an amazing boyfriend and many pets"—and CMT. Her grandmother, aunt, and mom are also diagnosed. Check out her blog at perseveringmomma.com.

Donna DeWick of beatinglimitations.com exemplifies the right attitude, nutrition, and activity levels, and manages the impact of CMT on her life. I find her blog posts inspirational and hope you will too.

I enjoy the website of crafting artist Sam Lewis of the crippledcrafter.co.uk, all the way across "the pond." She blogs for CMT Awareness Month about coping with daily life and trying to raise awareness and does a great job describing the symptoms and treatments.

Jill Price has a monthly and up-to-date column titled "CMT and Me" at charcot-marie-toothnews.com and shares wonderful stories, thought-provoking advice, and lots of encouragement. It is definitely recommended.

Other Disability Blogs

Type the following into your browser: Top 75 Disability Blogs & Websites For Disabled People To Follow in 2020, and then you can subscribe to have the blogs emailed directly to your inbox. I believe this is the motherlode of disability blogs, a great resource to me personally. It's amazing what I've learned by reading some of my favorites, and I might just become one of their contributing bloggers. Heaven knows I enjoy writing and sharing information. But I think I might be able to bring something new to the table by blogging about the therapeutic value of CMT and horseback riding. I might even blog about the satisfaction of volunteering at an animal shelter.

Regardless, I recommend you check out the 75 Top Disability blogs and see if something resonates with you not just as a reader but as a potential blogger yourself. And you can also check out healthcentral.com to read up on topics and conditions—the articles are great.

Guide to Physical and Occupational Therapy

Although there is no official drug treatment for CMT, physical therapy and moderate activity can help maintain muscle strength, endurance and flexibility. Occupational therapy and adaptive devices can assist in daily living.

A CMTA Guide to Physical and Occupational Therapy can be downloaded at https://www.cmtausa.org/news/a-guide-to-physical-and-occupational-therapy-for-cmt/.

Quest Magazine

I subscribe to Quest Magazine and find it quite useful. I found an article in the Research and Clinical Trials Update section about encouraging results in a CMT1A study. It revealed the first evidence that PXT3003 was safe, well-tolerated and showed a similar safety profile, as seen in an earlier Phase 2 study.

The magazine includes practical information as well, and from the perspective of people with disabilities. One article described the three things that "able bodies" take for granted and made some good points, especially about falling in the shower. I have an intense fear of that scenario and have come close, but I was able to grab the bars in the shower and steady myself. Getting around in hotel rooms, out of your normal area, is another topic I can relate to. I have a hard time with that sometimes, depending on how the room is laid out.

CMT Journal

This online and mobile-friendly resource shares inspiring stories, news, research, tools, books, links and videos, with the tagline: Everything we know about Charcot-Marie-Tooth. I can pull it up on my smart devices if I happen to be in waiting rooms and want to read articles.

Ask the Expert

The Hereditary Neuropathy Foundation has a section called Ask the Expert. Many people with CMT visit this site to get information first before going to a doctor. Some people realize they have to be their own advocate with CMT because the doctors don't know enough. I noticed that HNF has kept up with the latest medical news, including COVID-19 news.

Patient Advocacy

The Coalition of Patient Advocacy Groups (CPAG) is the patient advocacy arm of the Rare Diseases Clinical Research Network (RDCRN). In this role, patients groups serve as liaisons to their patient communities, ensuring two-way communication between consortium investigators and patient representatives and advising on issues of concern to the patient group, including study design, informed consent and research priorities.

U.S. Department of Health

The U.S. Department of Health's website, under the Disability Resources section, says, "People with disabilities need good jobs too, and several U.S. Department of Labor (DOL) agencies assist people with disabilities in seeking meaningful work and succeeding once on the job."

Oh, my gosh. This site has excellent information on Title I of the ADA, including the Title I of the Workforce Innovation and Opportunity Act, facts about the Americans with Disabilities Act, Section 503 of the Rehabilitation Act, employment provisions of the Title I of the ADA, Section 508 (technology accessibility for people with disabilities), Section 188 WIOA Nondiscrimination and Equal Opportunity Regulations, and the Employment and Training Administration.

Disability Resource Community

The Disability Resource Community at www.disabilityresource.org is another recommended resource—a platform designed for people with disabilities, their family members and caregivers to ask questions, share resources and build a community around the things that matter most. The site gives readers an opportunity to become contributors and send in articles (another chance for those of us who love to write to give back.)

Topics range from employment to advocacy to accommodations to assistive technology and much more, including legal resources. I saw a post on "Mental Health and Anxiety Apps" and another on "An Open Letter to Restaurateurs and Restaurant Staff," just to name a few very interesting perspectives. The site also provides a "search for an event" section to help those of us with disabilities connect with people and places.

Federal Disability Resources

I found a comprehensive list of federal disability resources at the American Association of Health and Disability at www.aahd.us/public-policy/federal-disability-resources/ that you might find useful. Check out the National Center on Public Health Resource Center for People with Disabilities under the site's Resource Center page as well. It has a list of abstracts and academic topics.

Agencies for Disabilities

I admit I wasn't aware of the many agencies and organizations for disabilities available to us. After a bit of research, I put together the following list that might help with human rights, employment, fair housing, accessibility, disorders, and education (you may find more).

- Department of Social Services
- Equal Employment Opportunity Commission
- Foundation for Peripheral Neuropathy
- Fundamental Rights Agency
- Genetic and Rare Diseases Information Center (GARD)
- Job Accommodation Network
- National Center for Biotechnology Information
- National Human Genome Research Institute
- National Institute of Neurological Disorders and Stroke
- National Institute on Disability, Independent Living, and Rehabilitation Research (NIDILRR)
- National Organization for Rare Disorders
- National Council on Disability
- Office of Disability Employment Policy
- Office of Fair Housing and Equal Opportunity
- Social Security Administration
- United States Department of Labor
- United States Office of Personnel Management
- U.S. Department of Education
- United States Access Board
- United States Department of Veterans Affairs
- United States Department of Justice, Civil Rights Division

Women's Resources

Believe it or not, the American College of Obstetricians and Gynecologists (ACOG) has some great information under their "WEBTREATS: Resources for Women with Disabilities" section.

Topics include "ACOG: Women with Disabilities," "Reproductive Health Care for Women with Disabilities," "The Arc," "Center for Research on Women with Disabilities," "Centers for Disease Control and Prevention—Women and Disabilities," "CDC: Right to Know Campaign," "Independent Living Research Utilization," "Medicine Plus Disabilities," and

"Through the Looking Glass."

Joss Kendrick, American Girl Doll

Perhaps you have heard of Melissa Shang. As a young teen with CMT, she petitioned American Girl to create dolls with disabilities in 2016. "For once, I don't want to be invisible or a side character that the main American Girl has to help: I want other girls to know what it's like to be me, through a disabled American Girl's story," Melissa said in the petition.

In 2019, American Girl consulted with the Hearing Loss Association of America and Olympic surfer Caroline Marks to create the character of Joss Kendrick, the first American Girl doll with a physical disability which happens to be congenital hearing loss.

Perhaps American Girl will circle back to Melissa Shang's idea and actually create a doll with muscular dystrophy or CMT. Wouldn't it be great to have a doll representative of girls who have a rare disease, spreading awareness in a new and novel way? Interestingly, Melissa wrote the book Mia Lee is Wheeling Through Middle School about herself as a spunky sixth grader with a wheelchair and a love for stop motion animation. She navigates the ins and outs of middle school angst and runs for video production club president. Great book—I list it below with additional recommended reading.

Books and Movies

I believe reading is beneficial to mind, body and spirit. You might want to check out the following books that share various CMT journeys—the last two are written for children. I'm sure there are more available, but these happen to be my top picks.

While you are at it, you can view a pretty incredible movie, "Bernadette," on Amazon Prime as well:

- *A Limp of Faith: Memoir of a Disabled Disciple* by Suzanne Rood
- *The Tribe of the Thin Ankles: Surviving, Striving and Thriving with Charcot-Marie-Tooth Disease* by Clark Semmes
- *Running for My Life, Winning for CMT* by Christine Wodke
- *CMT and Me: An intimate 75-year journey of love, loss and refusal to surrender to a disabling disease* by Linda D. Crabtree
- *Arlene on the Scene* by Carol Liu
- *Mia Lee is Wheeling Through Middle School* by Melissa Shang
- The movie "Bernadette" starring John A. Scarduzio and Bernadette

Scarduzio

Cookbooks for Chronic Illnesses

For those who can cook and enjoy taste-testing different meals, these books come recommended on Book Riot. I can't say I've tried them all, but I am inspired to explore the recipes.

- *The Anti-Inflammation Diet And Recipe Book: Protect Yourself And Your Family From Heart Disease, Arthritis, Diabetes, Allergies – And More* by Dr. Jessica Black
- *Great Taste, No Pain* by Sherry Brescia
- *Meals That Heal Inflammation: Embrace Healthy Living and Eliminate Pain, One Meal At A Time* by Julie Daniluk
- *The Autoimmune Paleo Cookbook: Manage Chronic Illness with Quick, Easy, and Flavorful Recipes* by Heather Puente
- *The Everything Healthy Meal Prep Cookbook* by Tina Chow
- *Healthy Cookbook for Two* by Rockridge Press,
- *The Laura Lea Balanced Cookbook* by Laura Lea Goldberg
- *The How Can It Be Gluten Free Cookbook* by America's Test Kitchen
- *The How Can It Be Gluten Free Cookbook Volume 2* by America's Test Kitchen
- *The Grain Brain Cookbook* by David Perlmutter, M.D. & Zoë François
- *The Easy Gluten-Free Cookbook* by Lindsay Garza
- *The Gluten Free Cookbook for Families* by Pamela Ellgen
- *Gluten-Free on a Shoestring* by Nicole Hunn
- *The Real Paleo Diet Cookbook* by Loren Cordain, Ph.D.
- *Danielle Walker's Against All Grain* by Danielle Walker
- *Danielle Walker's Against All Grain Celebrations* by Danielle Walker
- *One-Pot Paleo* by Jenny Castaneda
- *Paleo Slow Cooker Cookbook* by Shon Brooks
- *The Alternative Autoimmune Cookbook* by Angie Alt with Jenifer Beehler
- *The Essential AIP Cookbook* by Louise & Jeremy Hendon

- *Autoimmune Paleo Cookbook & Action Plan* by Rockridge Press
- *The Wahls Protocol* by Terry Wahls, M.D. with Eve Adamson
- *Allergy-Free and Easy Cooking* by Cybele Pascal
- *The Allergen-Free Baker's Handbook* by Cybele Pascal
- *The Allergy-Free Pantry* by Colette Martin
- *The Allergy-Free Family Cookbook* by Fiona Heggie & Ellie Lux
- *The Complete Allergy-Free Comfort Foods Cookbook* by Elizabeth Gordon

CHAPTER 19
OUT OF THE PAST AND INTO THE FUTURE

Life can only be understood backwards; but it must be lived forwards.
~ Søren Kierkegaard

Several people over the years have asked me if I have ever considered counseling people with disabilities. I would certainly like to be a counselor if I ever have the courage, strength and resources to certify. I'm fascinated with the concept because I do have experience being on the other end of counseling sessions, which were very helpful and put personal issues and challenges into proper context.

While my role right now is not counseling, I'm very busy advocating for people with disabilities. Perhaps I should have titled this chapter "Advocacy," for that's what it really encapsulates. Now, on a very large platform, I've put myself "out there" as someone who speaks on behalf of a cause—of CMT and the patients and families who must navigate the world from that perspective. But I also speak up on behalf of those that suffer abuse, whether it be through bullying or family dysfunction.

Abuse

People with disabilities are not automatically treated kindly by their parents or families. In fact, I've been to counseling for everything I went through in my childhood. I had to work through very personal and painful experiences, mostly having to do with the mentally abusive actions of my dad that I've endured my whole life. It's difficult to share these recollections. Doing so causes a lot of ambivalence; I love my father and am grateful for his financial investment in my life. But, I fear my father and have been damaged by him… damage that had to be undone through counseling.

There's also the feeling of disloyalty when talking about private matters. Confessionals made out in the open can be risky. Sometimes people judge those who have less than perfect family dynamics. Certainly, culture teaches us to remain quiet and not make a spectacle of our circumstances. But I feel compelled to explain how abuse can exacerbate disabilities, making it more difficult to function and cope.

My hope is that by sharing this intimate story, it will help anyone who has been broken. Sometimes we need to feel that we are not alone, and reading about how others navigated abuse can help piece us back together. Perhaps my situation will help someone find closure. Perhaps it will help others process their resentments and possibly even break generational cycles of abuse. I think that in order to go into the future, we have to resolve the past, and so I'm mentioning these counseling sessions in this chapter. Thankfully, I've come a long way.

The raw truth is not pretty. The counselor said, basically, that Dad was a mental abuser. There was really nothing I could do about it, but the counselor encouraged me to journal everything. Writing can be so therapeutic. I finally confronted my dad about our unhealthy relationship when the counselor requested he come to a session with me. Dad wouldn't go and told me it was all on me.

"Why?" I asked.

Dad countered with a question of his own: "Why have you hung that noose around my neck as a mental abuser?"

I answered, "Because that's what you are."

We had a knockdown drag-out fight, but he didn't hit me. I wondered if he would, based on his past behavior. One time when I was a kid, Dad threw me into my sliding closet doors. I had a canopy bed like most kids back in the '80s with a poster on the ceiling. Dad happened to lie down and said, "Gee, you have a really nice bed." Then he saw my teen idol poster on the ceiling—a poster of a shirtless male star from a teen magazine. That's why he threw me into the closet doors.

Once when I was little, sitting in the backseat of the car, Dad jumped all over me about something. I can't remember what I did to spark his rage; my aunt later recalled that I said, "I hate him. I hate him. I hate him!" Through the years, Dad got triggered over the most innocuous things, like wearing corkscrew earrings. "Why do you want to look like a whore?" he asked me. I was in 8th or 9th grade, and I was just wearing them because they were in style, I thought to myself. I had to take them out. I look back now and think, *Why in the world?* He didn't make my life easy. Sadly, my Mom knew what I went through with my father and did nothing about any of it. I think she has Stockholm Syndrome because she's been with him so long and thinks that's the way of life. She wanted to keep him from getting angrier, so she went along with almost everything he said. When she isn't around Dad, she acts like my normal mom. It is always very therapeutic to get away from Dad and just be around her because she is always worried about Dad and can't enjoy herself when he is present. Her sisters even say she can't relax much when she visits them because she worries about him or gets phone calls from him.

Don't get me wrong; my mother is nice to me. She lives next door, but my father's inability to accept me for who I am and what I have accomplished has put a wall between us. I barely see her; however, she is a big part of my support system, and we text a lot. I just wish we could visit more, but he makes it impossible unless someone else who he approves of stays with him.

I hope that one day my dad can evolve and find peace with himself and his loved ones, before it is too late. All I know is that it has taken quite a bit of therapy to get to a place of peace myself. Now I think, *Trust yourself. You've survived a lot, and you'll survive whatever is coming.*

Ryan's Legacy

Overall, Ryan dealt with life's obstacles amazingly well, including his CMT diagnosis. He knew what he was supposed to do to maintain or improve his health, but tried to get out of it sometimes, as kids are prone to do. He did begin to work harder in order to be better at the things he enjoyed. I worked with him constantly on the notion of perseverance so that it would become a critical part of his values. I believe this was accomplished as I watched him grow through the years. He showed great character in dealing with his CMT.

Now my mind is wandering back to some of my fondest memories, and I'm pretty sure they were some of Ryan's fondest memories too. When he first got his driver's license, he drove most of the way to South Dakota—just him and me. What a great mother-son trip that was, with plenty of time to talk about his hopes, dreams and aspirations. We enjoyed lots of music—Ryan was a music fanatic and a good traveler. He visited Disney World a total of three to four times, the first time in a stroller and the second time when he was older on spring break when my mom surprised him the second day because he kept begging her to go. His maw-maw, that's what he called his dad's mom, joined us on another trip. He loved his grandma and maw-maw very much. He also visited our timeshare in Branson, Missouri, as well as Las Vegas with his dad.

The San Antonio River Walk is a challenge for anyone, but Ryan loved it. He went down the Guadalupe River with his dad a few times. We went camping a lot and owned an RV when he was younger. He loved the outdoors, and a couple of times, we found parks that were off the beaten path. Just writing this takes me back to his kindergarten year and a special leaf project. We searched for different leaves, him eagerly finding just the right ones. I just loved that little boy, and I loved the young man he grew up to be.

My mother surprised me recently with a text. She ordered a stone to be placed under the flags on her property, engraved with the words:

Our hearts still ache in sadness,
and secret tears still flow.
What it meant to lose you,
no one will ever know.

In memory of our Grandson Ryan
7/19/98 – 12/25/18

Just before New Year's Day, Frank lacquered a wooden rose he had given me, turning it red. On New Year's Day, we visited the stone at my mother's home and laid the wooden rose there.

I feel my role is also to keep my son's memory alive and note here that I donated some of Ryan's possession to the community so he will be remembered in different ways and places. Talking about Ryan ensures he won't be forgotten, and I handle his loss through this prayer, along with many tears:

Lord, when plans change, help us to move forward with strength, always seeking out ways to make a difference in this world.

The Wrap Up

I treasure one additional insight from my wonderful friend Amy Anderson Gerlach, who was Ryan's godmother and a support system during the most difficult times of this journey.

Dawn's disease continues to progress, but as always, she gets up every day determined not to let it keep her down. It takes a lot of courage to walk down the halls of high school while teenage boys fling coins at you. It takes a lot of courage to get up on a 1,200 pound horse and tell him what you'd like him to do. It takes incredible strength to get out of bed the day after you've buried your only son. Dawn has done all of this and more and continues to do it because Charcot Marie Tooth simply will not tell her that she can't.

My friend has taught me so much just in the way she keeps on keeping on. I have not always been a good friend, and I don't know that I've always deserved her friendship. I do know that I'm so grateful that she has stuck by me and has allowed me to be part of her life. My life is so much fuller with her in it.

***

I hope you have been moved by this book. It has taken more than a year to write, starting as a joint project with my late son and becoming a means to share his wonderful spirit posthumously. But it also gives a raw and real bird's-eye view of the highs and lows of living with the disease. Everyone's CMT journey is different, but the common bond is courage and perseverance. Perhaps the words on these pages will inspire you to be extra kind to those with disabilities. Perhaps it will inspire you to spread CMT awareness or even fundraise for the cause.

Most of all, my fondest wish is that it bolsters your faith in our Almighty God, who comforts us in our trials on earth, never promising that our paths will be easy, but always remaining with us throughout. He answers prayers in amazing ways.

May God bless and keep you.

ABOUT THE AUTHOR

Dawn Johnson is an author and advocate for CMT awareness. She was born in Maryland and grew up in New Jersey, and navigates the world through the lens of the disease after being diagnosed at age twelve. She passed this hereditary condition to her son and only child, Ryan. Today she is the mother of an angel, for Ryan died on Christmas 2018 at the age of twenty due to complications of lymphocytic myocarditis.

Dawn earned a Bachelor of Science with a concentration in business administration and marketing from Rider University and graduated in three and a half years. She is a successful and experienced horseback riding instructor who is certified to teach therapeutic lessons. She owned Rockin D's Riding Center from 1992 to 2015 and taught Western, English and therapeutic riding lessons to people of all ages while living with CMT. She also boarded horses and kept abreast of the latest in animal nutrition.

Due to the complications of her disease, Dawn isn't in the saddle these days (something she misses) and works as an administrative assistant at WFI, a business owned and operated by her family. Her goal in publishing this book is to encourage others who live with CMT, and also speak up for the rights and dignity of those with disabilities. She wants to help people who live with this and other rare diseases and their caregivers in an entertaining as well as informative manner.

Please visit the "Dawn Johnson, Author" Facebook page to keep up with the book, written in tribute to her son Ryan, who was involved in the writing of the memoir until his sudden passing. It offers a very personal glimpse into a courageous mother-child journey.